BUILDING ANTIOCH

Your Role in a **TRANSFORMATIONAL CHURCH**

JEFF IORG

LifeWay Press®
Nashville, Tennessee

Published by LifeWay Press®

ISBN 978-1-4158-6985-7
Item 005371693

Dewey decimal classification: 262.7
Subject headings: BIBLE. N.T. ACTS 11--STUDY \ CHURCH

This book is a resource for credit in the Christian Growth Study Plan.
For information, please visit *www.lifeway.com/CGSP.*

To order additional copies of this resource: write to LifeWay Church Resources Customer Service; One LifeWay Plaza; Nashville, TN 37234-0113;
fax (615) 251-5933; phone toll free (800) 458-2772; e-mail *orderentry@lifeway.com;*
order online at *www.lifeway.com*; or visit the LifeWay Christian Store serving you.

Printed in the United States of America

Leadership and Adult Publishing
LifeWay Church Resources
One LifeWay Plaza
Nashville, TN 37234-0175

BUILDING
ANTIOCH

About the Author

DR. JEFF IORG is the president of Golden Gate Baptist Theological Seminary. Prior to his service at the seminary, Dr. Iorg was the Executive Director of the Northwest Baptist Convention for almost 10 years. He was also the founding pastor of Greater Gresham Baptist Church in Gresham, Oregon, and has served as a pastor in Missouri and a staff pastor in Texas.

Dr. Iorg teaches leadership, preaching, and church ministry courses at Golden Gate. He speaks frequently on these same subjects in conferences and other venues, including college campuses and leadership seminars. His publications include four books—*The Case for Antioch: A Biblical Model for a Transformational Church, The Painful Side of Leadership, The Character of Leadership,* and *Is God Calling Me?*—along with dozens of articles and curriculum materials. Dr. Iorg maintains a leadership resources website at *www.JeffIorg.com*.

Dr. Iorg is a graduate of Hardin Simmons University (B.A.), Midwestern Baptist Theological Seminary (M.Div.), and Southwestern Baptist Theological Seminary (D.Min.). He is married to Ann and has three adult children. His hobbies include umpiring baseball, reading, and searching for the world's best barbecue restaurant. His personal ministry includes outreach to the professional baseball community in the San Francisco Bay Area.

Antioch and You

One church can change the world. That statement might sound idealistic, especially when the problems of churches have been so publicly proclaimed in recent years. In fact, given the reputation of the church, many Christians have been tempted to give up on the church, treating it as an optional part of spiritual growth and development.

You would have a hard time selling that attitude to the believers at Antioch. This New Testament church stands as a shining example of what might be. The Christians in Antioch were an unlikely group of Christ-followers—raised in a pluralistic and polytheistic culture, living in a multicultural urban melting pot with little to no knowledge of the God of the Jews. Despite all of this, the church at Antioch remains one of the most innovative and transformational churches in history. We could say that most churches outside of Jerusalem might not have ever been started if not for the church in Antioch.

Does that sound like your church? If the answer is no, then take heart, because you, along with others in your church, can begin *Building Antioch* in your community. Over six sessions, you will dig into the attributes of the Antioch fellowship that enabled it to be a transformational church. Each session, you will examine a particular characteristic that made the church at Antioch so unique. You'll discover how to become a believer who embodies that characteristic, and then you'll see how to help your church become a place characterized by these attributes.

Here's how it works:

This study includes both opportunities for individual and group study. At the beginning of each session, you will find the guide for the small-group portion of the study. You can make the most of your group experience with *Building Antioch* using the following outline:

- **Lay the Foundation:** Greet one another, pray, and discuss the previous week's devotions using the questions (15 min.).
- **Frame the Discussion**: Watch the discussion-starter video from the DVD and discuss the questions provided in the group experience (10-15 min.). Then watch the teaching video from the DVD (10 min.) while filling out the listening guide. Discuss the DVD segment and questions provided in the group experience (15-20 min.). Close with prayer.
- **Finishing Touches**: The group experience wraps up with a key verse to memorize and some specific challenges for the upcoming week.

Continue your study of *Building Antioch* by completing the five personal devotions following the group experience to reinforce the content studied in the group experience.

Throughout the study, you'll be challenged by the people of Antioch and their love for God, each other, and the world. You will find hope and resolve to play your own part in building a transformational church in your community. Begin praying now, and believe that God is still at work taking ordinary people and building them into those who change the world.

SESSION 1

What Is a Transformational Church?

SESSION 1

LAY THE FOUNDATION

1. Introduce yourself, and share one fact about yourself to help your group get to know you better.

2. Share what you hope to gain from this study.

3. What three words come to mind when you think about what the church should be? Why?

4. What three words come to mind when you think about the current state of the church? Is there a difference? Why?

FRAME THE DISCUSSION

Watch the discussion starter on the DVD then discuss the following questions with your group.

1. What is the church?

2. Why might answering that question be important?

3. On the scale below, how would you rate your current attitude about the church? Share your answer with the group.

   Pessimistic •———————o Optimistic

4. Do you remember anything specific about the congregation at Antioch? What do you recall?

Watch the teaching segment from the DVD using the viewer guide below.

Antioch is a STRONG model for the future church.

Obstacles in Urban Ministry:

1. Cities are OUTPOSTS of EVIL
2. Constant change
3. EXPENSIVE

Antioch

1. Large city 500K - 800K population
2. Remarkable LOCATION
3. Unique GOVERNMENT
4. Diverse religious practices
5. Multicultural collection of people

The city of Antioch REPRESENTS and REMINDS us of cities today.

The Church has always been God's PLAN in every setting.

Confidence in the GOSPEL.
BE A transformational church.

Discuss the teaching segment with your group using the questions below.

1. Do you tend to have a realistic view of New Testament churches? Why or why not?
They were NOT perfect.
History

2. If Paul were writing a letter to your church, what are some of the things you think he might address?

OUTREACH, commitment, speck tators, power of prayer, LISTEN TO Holy SPIRIT, Teachable spirit — compliment care for each other – step out in faith

3. Given what you heard on the video, why do you think the church at Antioch is worth studying?

They DID things RIGHT,

4. Read Acts 11:19-26 with your group. Based on this reading, what characteristics set the church at Antioch apart from other early churches? Grace of GOD at work, spoke to both Jews + Greeks outreach focus on Good News of LJC

Close with prayer.

Eph 3:10 memorize

Emotional + Spiritual life are interconnected
The Law challenges us to test our faith

FINISHING TOUCHES

Scripture Memory

> "This is so God's multi-faceted wisdom may now be made known through the church to the rulers and authorities in the heavens."
> **Ephesians 3:10**

Building Antioch

- Write a note of encouragement to your pastor or other church leader expressing your belief and commitment to your church.
- Pray for your pastor by name each day this week.
- Look for specific ways you might begin to serve in your church to help it move closer to God's vision for what the church might be.

Video sessions are available for purchase at *www.lifeway.com/buildingantioch*

SESSION 1

What Is a Transformational Church?

Church. There's a word with some baggage! Ask people their opinions about church, and you'll hear an explanation of an institution, a defense of their faith, or—occasionally—a high level of personal commitment. Ask others and you'll find loathing, frustration, or a litany of complaints. The opinions regarding church are often divided, even among Christians.

Some Christians believe the church, by nature, is a flawed organization since it's made up of human beings, and the best option is simply to accept the church's inherent shortcomings. Others see those shortcomings as a call to abandonment and conclude there's really no need to be a part of a church at all.

Neither of these opinions fit. The church is God's eternal plan, the summation of His redemptive work and its glorification in the culmination of history. Local churches, warts and all, are God's strategy for advancing His kingdom. We cannot abandon our commitment to that with which God has closely aligned Himself.

On the other hand, however, we can't accept without question or challenge the areas where so many churches fall short. We must, as individual believers, actively engage the church in an effort to see local bodies become all they were created to be.

When we choose to do that, we won't see perfect churches, just as we don't find perfect individuals making up those churches. We will, however, begin to see churches with renewed vision, passion, and power to transform the lives of their members and communities, even to the ends of the earth.

So let's start there, with the church. We need to realize what the church is in order to understand how it can be transformational.

Day 1 The Big Picture

Imagine the following scenario. You are part of a group of people in an area of the world largely unreached with the gospel. It's not that people haven't heard about Jesus; it's that the message of the gospel hasn't yet been understood and embraced. So you and a few other like-minded Christians decide to start a church. You begin to meet people in the community, telling them about your new church. They are interested, but they tend to have the same question: "Why do I need to be part of a church?"

How would you respond to that question?

Is being part of a church necessary for every Christian? Why or why not?

These questions are important for us to consider. They get to the core of what we really believe about the church. But in order to answer those questions, some other things must also be taken into consideration. Let's begin with the most basic question of all:

What is "the church"?

Is there a difference between *the* church and your local church? If so, what is it?

How are the two related?

In Ephesians, Paul addressed the nature and importance of the church. In his description, we see there's far more at stake in understanding the church than just the names on a roll sheet or being a part of a supportive spiritual family.

Read Ephesians 3:8-12. According to this passage, what is the church?

In Paul's mind, how important is the church? Why?

The church is God's ultimate purpose for the universe. Creating humankind, redeeming believers, and sustaining them as His eternal companions is God's ultimate purpose for all He has done or will do. The church is the "administration of the mystery hidden for ages in God who created all things" (Eph. 3:9). God has always had a plan. His plan was a "mystery"—not a whodunit, but something so profound it's incomprehensible apart from God.

What do you think this "mystery" is?

What makes it so incomprehensible apart from God?

What does the text mean when it says the church is the "administration" of that mystery?

For eons, God kept His mystery as private knowledge hidden within Himself—a true top secret plan. But through the church, it has been revealed. God's intention was to send Jesus, the Messiah, with His "incalculable riches" (Eph. 3:8) revealed to and in His followers. Amazingly, it's in the church—your church—this plan is revealed. The cantankerous coots, snotty-nosed kids, pimply teenagers, and balky matrons are all part of God's eternal treasure. The painstaking effort God made to create an entire cosmos devoted to this one purpose boldly underscores the importance of the church. *Of your church.*

Is it difficult for you to believe your church is part of the revelation of God's eternal mystery? Why or why not?

The fact that we, as flawed and sinful humanity, are part of God's church accentuates His incredible grace and wisdom. Paul said God's "multi-faceted" wisdom is revealed through the church. Imagine holding a precisely cut diamond up to a light and turning it slowly. The facets reveal different shades, shapes, and qualities of the stone. In the same way, the church encompasses God's expansive work in the world. The church is a multicultural, multinational, multilingual, and multigenerational organism revealing God's complexity and infinite capacity to relate to all people.

There is nothing else like the church in all creation, and as such, the church gives us a glimpse of God's wisdom and His capacity to conceive, create, oversee, and relate to the endless variety of the universe.

Read Ephesians 3:8-12 again. To whom is the wisdom of God in the church revealed?

Why would such a revelation be necessary?

How does that audience add to the importance of the church?

According to Paul, the church is on display before the "rulers and authorities in the heavens" (Eph. 3:10). These beings of the spiritual realm are stopped in their tracks by the church. Upon its revelation, a holy hush might have fallen on all of them as they collectively thought, "Well, we never saw that coming." God's mysterious plan for redeeming people was made known through the church.

The church astounded both angels and demons when it was revealed. Aspects of God's person and plan, not previously known or anticipated, are now fully displayed.

Given this eternal significance of the church, how can we possibly think of turning our back on the revelation of God's wisdom? We must recapture a sense of wonder when looking at the church. That's wonder the angels and the demons have—and we should too!

What are your predominant emotions as you look at your church?

How might God want to change your vision for your church?

Day 2 The First Church

At first glance, it doesn't seem like a well thought-out plan. The leaders of the first church had no formal training. They didn't have a manual or even a model to base their efforts. They had no mentors to train them in strategic methods of engaging their communities with the gospel. They were, in every sense of the word, ordinary people. Yet their gathering as the church was the beginning of the complete outworking of God's redemptive plan through Christ.

Put yourself in the place of those first church leaders. What thoughts or questions might have gone through your mind?

Why do you think Jesus intentionally entrusted ordinary people with carrying out His mission? What advantage might their commonness have given them?

Does that give you hope for the potential of your church? Why or why not?

When Jesus launched His earthly ministry, He assembled twelve disciples as the foundation for creating the church. Though they didn't realize it at the time, He was equipping these ordinary men to carry on after His resurrection. When He ascended, He instructed His followers about their responsibility to spread the gospel. The Book of Acts is a history of the highlights of their obedience to Jesus' command.

Read Acts 1:8. What specific components did their mission involve?

How might Acts 1:8 relate to the future of the church as a whole?

For your church, what areas correspond to those mentioned in Acts 1:8?

- **Jerusalem:**
- **Judea:**
- **Samaria:**
- **Ends of the earth:**

Who would have expected much from such men? True, they spent time with Jesus, but it didn't erase the fact that they were common men from small villages. But by the end of the Book of Acts, they had led a movement—a movement of churches—that had turned the world upside down.

It began on the Day of Pentecost, when the Holy Spirit flooded the hearts of every believer. The Spirit came in such overwhelming power and marked the dawning of the church, indwelled by the constant presence of the Holy Spirit from that point forward. Peter preached both the bad news and the good news—the crowd had crucified the Son of God and yet He had risen from the dead and was offering them forgiveness and life. The results of that message were astounding.

Based on the Book of Acts, how important was the influence of the Holy Spirit in the early church? How do you know?

Do you see the same emphasis on the Spirit today? Why or why not?

Read Acts 2:41-47. What characterized the church in those days?

What part of that description is the most intriguing to you? Why?

When we read such a description of church life, we might feel uplifted and discouraged at the same time. Who could not be impressed by their generosity, fellowship, and worship? What an amazing time it must have been.

On the other hand, you might be downcast because your church doesn't exactly match the description from Acts 2:41-47. Or does it? We tend to be overly critical of the church. Many churches are living out the realities of the biblical model—as appropriate in their cultural setting. The fact that you have a local church at all is a miraculous testimony to the durability of God's plan. Two thousand years is quite a track record for longevity. Throughout Acts, imperfections in the church appear. But even with those shortcomings, the early church grew and prospered. Your church can do the same.

The record of the early church contains many examples of organizational mismanagement, poor leadership, doctrinal division, and waning missional commitment. Nevertheless, the church endured—and still carries on today. Your church is an example and result of this endurance. Is there room for improvement? Certainly. But you can't deny God has been and continues transforming individuals and communities through the church.

What is one area of your church where you clearly see God at work?

When did you last thank God for your church?

Day 3 Expansion

The first church had their marching orders. Beginning in Jerusalem, the movement of the gospel was to spread beyond the city walls to the entire world. Jesus challenged the embryonic community of believers to extend their influence to Judea, Samaria, and eventually the ends of the earth.

What were the advantages for the first church starting in Jerusalem?

Was there anything strategic in Jesus' command to begin there?

What sort of spiritual background did most early converts have?

Given that, what was worship and teaching like in the first church?

Thanks to the miracle of Pentecost, the church was off and running with over three thousand added to their number on the first day. The Spirit continued to move, and daily more and more people believed in Jesus. This first church in Jerusalem was made up of people with a Jewish heritage, people already familiar with the God of Abraham, Isaac, and Jacob.

The apostles taught the people how Jesus was central to what they already knew from the Old Testament, how in Him all the law and the prophets were fulfilled. In Jerusalem, things went well during those early years. So well, in fact, the church did very little to pursue the rest of Jesus' Acts 1:8 commission. Through the first seven chapters of the Book of Acts, there wasn't much recorded effort by the church to extend the gospel outside the walls of Jerusalem.

Read again Acts 1:8. Why do you think the church was slow to move outside Jerusalem?

What would have been the difficulties in doing so?

There are numerous reasons why the first church might have been reluctant to expand its borders. Perhaps they felt they weren't prepared with enough knowledge or experience. Maybe they weren't financially able. Or maybe there were still some of the old biases hanging on in their belief systems.

For hundreds of years, Israel believed God had chosen them at the exclusion of all others to be His people. While the Jews were indeed God's chosen people, God's design was always to reveal Himself to Israel so they might, in turn, bless other nations as a kingdom of priests.

How would you write the job description for a priest in the days of the Old Testament?

Read Exodus 19:5-6. What do you think the phrase, "kingdom of priests" means?

How does this phrase relate to your church now?

God intended for Israel to be the bridge between Him and the rest of the world, just as a priest stands between a person and God. Far from being their national God, the Lord's intent was to make Himself known as the God of all nations—starting with Israel. Unfortunately, however, there were challenges of racial bias and cultural prejudice standing in the way.

As an example, read Acts 6:1. What was the problem in the church?

Are there any such problems in the church today? If so, what specifically?

How do biases and prejudices contradict the mission of the church?

Though the Greek widows were still Jews, the prejudice against them happened inside Jerusalem. Imagine, then, how difficult it was for the church to engage a people like the Samaritans, who were hated among Israelites. Even more so, consider the obstacles to moving out into a predominantly Gentile world.

Read Acts 8:1. What was the catalyst that made the church move out?

Is it surprising the Lord used persecution to accomplish His purposes? Why or why not?

Have you seen that principle at work in your life? How has God used surprising circumstances around you to accomplish His purposes?

When persecution fell on the church after the death of Stephen, the fledgling community could have collapsed. Instead, God used the tragedy to accomplish His goal of scattering the church and spreading the gospel far and wide.

Make no mistake—God will not rest until the gospel, carried by the church, goes to all people around the world. This has been His ultimate mission since choosing Israel as His special people. He has not relented in His quest to go global with the gospel.

How committed are you to the spread of the gospel?

Does your church reflect your attitude about spreading the gospel? If so, how?

What will you do to encourage greater passion for God's mission through your church?

Day 4 Let's Go to Antioch

The early church had difficulty moving beyond its predominantly Jewish origins. But prompted by the persecution of the church after the death of Stephen in Acts 7, the dispersed disciples started planting gospel seeds wherever they moved.

Acts 8 records the preaching of the gospel in Samaria and to the Ethiopian eunuch, a precursor to the gospel being preached to all people. Acts 10 bolsters the development of cross-cultural witnessing as Peter received a divinely-originated dream which resulted in his declaration: "I really understand that God doesn't show favoritism, but in every nation the person who fears Him and does righteousness is acceptable to Him" (Acts 10:34-35).

Up to this point, why might someone have accused God of showing favoritism?

Do you think your church is ever guilty of favoritism? If so, how?

Hot on the heels of the Gentile conversions recorded at the end of Acts 10, we encounter the first full-blown witness among Gentiles. It happened in Antioch—and the resulting church remains one of the most influential bodies of local believers in history.

Read Acts 11:19-22. Why did the Jerusalem church send someone to see what was happening at Antioch?

Do you remember anything about Barnabas? Why do you think he specifically was sent to Antioch?

Antioch was the third largest city in the Roman Empire with a population estimated between 500,000–800,000 people. Imagine a city that size before indoor plumbing, comprehensive sewage systems, and systematized garbage collection and disposal. It was located near the mouth of the Orontes River, about 15 miles from its port city of Seleucus, making Antioch both an inland city and a major seaport.[1] The location is now Antakya, Turkey, about 12 miles from the Syrian border.

Antioch had a prominent Greek heritage and was granted status as a "free city" by the Roman general Pompey. As such, it had limited self-government and some exemption from provincial taxes. Antioch became the capital of the Roman province of Syria in 23 B.C.[2] The city was also famous for its religious practices as the area was a cult center for many Greek gods. Antioch was a center for the worship of Zeus, Poseidon, Adonis, and Tyche—a cosmopolitan city of religious pluralism worshiping a pantheon of gods and goddesses.[3]

There was a small Jewish community living in this diverse city. Furthermore, Greeks, Syrians, Phoenicians, Jews, Persians, Arabs, and Italians were all also part of the city's population mix.[4] As a port city, a capital city, and a transportation hub, Antioch attracted all kinds of people creating a mosaic of nationalities, languages, and cultures.

Given this description, what sort of challenges would there have been for the gospel in Antioch?

Does Antioch sound similar to any major cities today? If yes, how so?

What characteristics might make Antioch a place where the gospel would flourish?

Read Acts 11:22-26. What did Barnabas find there?

Out of this jumble of culture and religion, God brought to life a community of faith in Him. God created the first Gentile church—proof that the gospel was for everyone. Alongside each other, people of different nationalities and languages worshiped Jesus Christ. They reached their neighbors, sent out missionaries, and solved doctrinal challenges. They were incredibly generous, sharing both material gifts and leaders with other churches. They were a community of spiritual power, a light shining in the dark world with little or no knowledge of Jesus.

Scripture records how far-reaching their impact was. The church at Antioch is a model of a transformational church, a family of people individually transformed by Jesus.

Using a concordance or *mybiblestudy.com*, look up other references to "Antioch." List below a few of the occurrences that happened there.

Which of these events grabs your imagination? Why?

Day 5 A Transformational Church

As in any modern city, there were challenges for the gospel in Antioch. But unlike many modern cities, the gospel thrived in Antioch. Then, as now, where people live in the greatest density, the problems of humanity intensify. Sin abounds in cities.

Do you agree with that assessment? Why do you think sin abounds in cities?

In what ways have you seen that assessment played out in cities you have lived or visited?

Where sin abounds, grace abounds all the more. Where grace abounds, the gospel transforms. As the gospel transforms individuals, congregations form to celebrate and spread the gospel. Antioch is an inspiring church that changed a city and today motivates us to do the same. No place is too large, too diverse, too religiously confused, or too sinful for the gospel. Churches can thrive in cities. Churches can transform cities.

This is the legacy of Antioch. This legacy makes that church stand apart from the other churches of the New Testament.

What three words first come to mind when you think about first-century churches?

1.

2.

3.

We tend to look at early churches through rose-colored glasses, as if they were perfect organizations filled with perfect people living in harmony with God and each other. A more careful study reveals a very different picture.

The church at Corinth had a member having an incestuous relationship with his stepmother. Their worship services were a three-ring circus with frivolous and irreverent public displays (see 1 Cor. 5). The church at Rome had profound doctrinal questions and struggled with practical problems like church and state relationships (see Rom. 13) and church fellowship and function issues (see Rom. 12). In the Galatian region, the churches battled over the nature of the gospel (see Gal. 1–2), the role of law (see Gal. 3), and freedom of conscience (see Gal. 5). The Ephesians were confused about the function of church leaders (see Eph. 4) and the nature of spiritual warfare (see Eph. 6). In Philippi, the church had fellowship issues characterized by two women in such conflict that they were singled out—by name! (See Phil. 4:2.)

That doesn't even include the Thessalonians, Colossians, and the churches mentioned in Revelation (see Rev. 2–3) who struggled with all manner of doctrinal problems and sinful behavior. In short, the New Testament churches were a diverse collection of sometimes dysfunctional believers trying to work out the messy first decades of community life in Christ. They looked very much like us.

Does this realistic look at the New Testament churches surprise you? Why or why not?

Does knowing these things make you hopeful or discouraged about your own church? Why?

Apart from the other New Testament churches stands the church at Antioch—a fellowship of transformed believers that overcame formidable obstacles to model healthy, balanced, effective life in a transformational church. The Bible shows us the reality of who we are and also the reality of who we can become.

In an unlikely setting, we see a group of people coming together to form a church characterized by spiritual power, an unwavering commitment to advance the gospel, a firm grasp of the truth, and extreme generosity. Let's dream a little bit together. Let's dream about what God wants to do in each one of us so we come together to see our churches live up to the legacy of Antioch.

Look again at the characteristics above for the church at Antioch: spiritual power, commitment to advance the gospel, a firm grasp of the truth, and generosity. Which of these characteristics do you most embody?

Which do you least embody?

In what ways might your church be a reflection of your own strengths and weaknesses?

1. John Polhill, *The New American Commentary* (Nashville, TN: Broadman Press, 1992) p. 268.
2. Ibid., 269.
3. Darrell Bock, *Acts: Baker Exegetical Commentary on the New Testament* (Grand Rapids, MI: Baker Academic, 2007), 413.
4. Ibid.

SESSION 2
Spiritual Power

SESSION 2:

LAY THE FOUNDATION

1. Look back at the daily devotions you completed this week. Share one particular insight that was meaningful to you with your group.

2. Given what you learned about the situation in the city of Antioch, are you surprised the church flourished the way it did? Why or why not? ACTS 11:13
NO – Because of Holy Spirit.

3. What are some of the defining characteristics you think the members of the church at Antioch possessed to build a church like this one?
focus on their purpose
NOT JUST LIMITED TO the Jews

FRAME THE DISCUSSION

Watch the discussion starter on the DVD then discuss the following questions with your group.

1. What ripples is your church causing? That is to say, in what parts of your community and the world is your church currently engaged? PRE-school, VBS
WITNESS in workplace; Shoeboxes, food pantry

2. When you think about a church of spiritual power, what comes to mind? POWER of God
growth

3. Do you think we typically view the Holy Spirit as powerful? Why or why not?

4. How important is the Holy Spirit in your life? How important is the Holy Spirit in the life of your church?
illuminates

Watch the teaching segment from the DVD using the viewer guide below.

For a church to experience the Holy Spirit, it must have members and leaders who are filled with the Holy Spirit.

When you are filled with the Holy Spirit, you come under the __________ of the Holy Spirit.

There is no __________ __________ for being filled with the Holy Spirit.

Aspects of Being Filled with the Spirit:

1. __________

Experiencing the filling of the Holy Spirit is more about __________ something within you than __________ something you don't already have.

2. __________

Being filled with the Spirit involves acquiescence of the heart to God.

acquiescence:
__________ __________

3. Changing __________ behavior

If you're not participating in spiritual disciplines, you are __________ the filling of the Holy Spirit in your life.

You grieve the Holy Spirit by __________ behavior.

4. __________

The Holy Spirit spoke through the __________ to the __________.

This was the first time a church banded together to send out a __________ team.

The church sent their __________ leaders.

Discuss the teaching segment with your group using the questions below.

1. Are any of the ways the Holy Spirit worked at Antioch surprising to you? Which one? Why?
2. Why does Paul write about a similarity between being drunk with wine and being filled with the Spirit?
3. Which aspect of being filled with the Spirit is most challenging to you? Why?
4. What are some ways you might more actively seek the filling of the Spirit?
5. What are some ways you might encourage your church to become a church of spiritual power?

Close with prayer.

FINISHING TOUCHES

Scripture Memory

"Don't be foolish, but understand what the Lord's will is. And don't get drunk with wine, which leads to reckless actions, but be filled by the Spirit."

Ephesians 5:17-18

Building Antioch

- Write down the aspects of being filled with the Spirit and post them where you will see them each morning. Then, pray through them before beginning your day.
- Exercise faith in the Spirit's filling by actively seeking one opportunity to share the gospel this week.
- Pray daily for your church to become a church of spiritual power.

Video sessions are available for purchase at *www.lifeway.com/buildingantioch*

SESSION 2

Spiritual Power

The New Testament is full of stories of spiritual power. The dead were raised to life, the sick were made well, the poor had their needs met, and the gospel triumphed in the face of incredible opposition. What an exciting time for early Christians!

Similar supernatural breakthroughs happened in the church at Antioch. There was an atmosphere of spiritual power among those early believers. Consequently, people were tuned into the work of God. They came together with a sense of expectation, knowing God was at work in and through them. The spiritual power of the individuals, and consequently the church at Antioch when they gathered corporately, was contagious. They developed a reputation as a church where God was changing lives.

The Holy Spirit wasn't an idea in Antioch; He was a vibrant part of their daily experience. He was vital to all aspects of church life—from worshiping to giving to serving to settling doctrinal and organizational problems.

In our day of complex church programs created and managed by professionally-trained ministers, advocating dependence on the Spirit to empower the church sounds outdated. Words like "anointing," "unction," and "filling" aren't common descriptors of modern church members or church ministries. We tend to measure churches the same way we measure individuals—on the externals. If an individual is well-dressed, earns a good income, and has a reasonably healthy family, we deem them successful. Similarly, if a church has adequate leaders, nice facilities, and well-organized programs, we look at them with favor.

A measure of personal and corporate success at your church can come from concentrated human effort. But real transformation—whether in an individual, through a church, or across a community—is generated and sustained by the Holy Spirit.

BUILDING
ANTIOCH

Day 1 The Spirit at Antioch

The Book of Acts is more the Acts of the *Holy Spirit* than the Acts of the *Apostles*. It's no surprise then that there are three specific references to the Holy Spirit in the story of the church at Antioch, as well as many implied references.

Read the following Scriptures. Beside each one, record the work ascribed to the Holy Spirit:

- **Acts 11:24:**
- **Acts 11:28:**
- **Acts 13:2:**

The work of the Spirit is implied throughout the Antioch narrative, even when the words "Holy Spirit" aren't included. For example, the Spirit no doubt superintended the preachers who boldly planted the gospel—and the resulting church—among the Gentile community in Antioch. The Spirit certainly sustained the church's continued support for mission work as it developed over the years. The absence of the words "Holy Spirit" in the text doesn't mean the Spirit wasn't involved. We can trust He was and still is involved in healthy churches.

The beginning point for experiencing spiritual power is having a right understanding and appreciation for the work of the Spirit. But for many Christians, the Holy Spirit is a mystery and has little to no bearing on their everyday lives. This is a serious error and contradicts the words of Jesus concerning the importance of the Holy Spirit.

Read John 16:5-15. Why, according to Jesus, was it for the benefit of the disciples that He go away?

Based on these verses, how important is the Holy Spirit?

Why do you think the Holy Spirit is called "the Counselor"? What are some other ways that word might be translated?

Jesus predicted great things in this passage. Preeminent among them was the coming of the Holy Spirit. The Spirit is the initiator of faith, the confronter of sinful behavior, and a guide into all truth. Through the Holy Spirit the disciples not only found spiritual power but also guidance and direction for the worldwide mission Jesus assigned them.

The Spirit, when He arrived, continued the work of Jesus, enabling early Christians to understand the fullness of their faith by continuing to teach them. Furthermore, the Spirit fulfilled one of God's long-held desires.

Read Exodus 25:1-8. Why was Moses to take an offering from the people?

What was God's desire in commanding the building of the tabernacle?

God desires intimacy with His people. The tabernacle was built inside the camp—in the midst of the people—symbolically reminding them of the nearness of God. Later, the temple was built in Jerusalem as another reminder of God's presence. Despite the nearness of the tabernacle (and later the temple), the people were still separated from God by their sin. In His holiness, God can't tolerate impurity in His presence.

But thanks to the sacrifice of Jesus, the barriers for intimacy with God have been removed. A new temple—the one made possible by Jesus' resurrection and the arrival of the Spirit—is far closer than those man-made facilities.

Read 1 Corinthians 6:19-20. What is the new temple?

What implications does the new temple have for the practical aspects of your life like eating, exercise, sleeping, recreation, and moral choices?

The church at Corinth was badly in need of this reminder. With gluttony, sexual perversion, and other bodily sins running rampant in their congregation, Paul reminded them the body is far more than our personal playground. The body serves the same purpose as the temple of old—to house the Spirit of the Lord.

The Holy Spirit is closer than any human companion to every Christian. He enters believers at the moment of salvation, never to depart. He guides in truth, convicts of sin, confirms our identity in Christ, and furthers our intimacy with the Lord. The appropriate question isn't,"Is the Holy Spirit is available to you as a believer?" The proper question is, "Are you experiencing the spiritual power already residing in you?"

How do you think we might more readily access the spiritual power at work in churches like Antioch?

Day 2 Filled with the Spirit

Barnabas had a solid reputation among first-century Christians. He pops up in pivotal situations, providing leadership and sharing wisdom, to continuously encourage the spread of the gospel. Such was his influence in the church at Antioch.

Read Acts 11:22-24. How is Barnabas described?

What do you think it would be like to meet Barnabas? What would he say? How would you feel after your conversation with him?

Do you know anyone who reminds you of Barnabas? Describe that person below.

Barnabas was originally sent from Jerusalem, in an apostolic role, to investigate the report of Gentiles becoming Christians in Antioch. Barnabas surveyed the situation, validated what was happening, and set about encouraging the fledgling believers in the city. Later, he was responsible for bringing Saul (Paul) from Tarsus, and the two of them went to work in Antioch making disciples and bringing structure to the developing church.

How was Barnabas able to be such a powerful influence for good? Part of the reason lies in his description in Acts 11:24, "He was a good man, *full of the Holy Spirit,* and of faith" (emphasis added).

Read Ephesians 5:15-18. Why do you think being filled with the Spirit is contrasted with being drunk on wine?

How does being under the influence of alcohol illustrate being filled with the Spirit?

To be filled with the Spirit means to be controlled by the Spirit, to be under His guiding influence. It means your will is submitted to the Spirit's leadership. You are no longer independent or self-reliant—no longer trusting your strength, judgment, intellect, or training. A person filled with the Holy Spirit has emptied himself, emulating Jesus in taking "the form of a slave" (Phil. 2:7), becoming a servant of the Spirit's desires, impulses, and urges. The importance of being filled with the Spirit can't be overstated.

Believers were filled with the Holy Spirit when the church was inaugurated (see Acts 2:4). Peter was filled while preaching (see Acts 4:8). The church was filled during a prayer meeting (see Acts 4:31). Stephen was filled at his martyrdom trial (see Acts 7:55-60). Based on these examples, how is a person filled with the Holy Spirit? It's not an easy question to answer. Despite these recorded occurrences, the process of how each filling happened is omitted.

How do you think someone is filled with the Holy Spirit?

Why do you think the Bible doesn't give an explicit process for how it happens?

In every case in the Bible, the result of the Spirit's filling is emphasized more than the process of filling.

> **For each Scripture below, write out the result of the Spirit's filling:**
> - Acts 2:4:
> - Acts 4:8-22:
> - Acts 4:31:
> - Acts 7:51-60:
> - Acts 9:17-18:
>
> **What patterns or general principles about the results of spiritual filling do you see in these examples?**

The fact that the Bible omits the process of being filled with the Spirit is intentional (in God's wisdom) to prevent formulaic incantations developing as a false means to pseudospiritual power. In short, there's no mantra to chant or script to memorize that guarantees a Spirit-filled life.

The most important insight is this: While there is no formula for being filled with the Spirit, the results of being filled are vital. Whether dying well, preaching with great boldness, or miraculous healing, being filled with the Spirit involves manifestations of supernatural power ending in the glory of God and the gospel's influence expanding.

Begin by praying toward this end—that you would have a fresh experience of spiritual power through the filling of the Holy Spirit.

BUILDING
ANTIOCH

Day 3 How to Be Filled

Paul was explicit in Ephesians 5:18: "Don't get drunk with wine, which leads to reckless actions, but be filled with the Spirit." In this verse, the apostle issues a command. It's as forceful a command as might be found elsewhere in the New Testament, as clear as "Run from sexual immorality" (1 Cor. 6:18) and "Be doers of the word and not hearers only" (Jas. 1:22). The problem is, as we've already stated, the Bible gives no specific formula for being filled with the Spirit.

While there's no specific formula, principles can be discerned from various biblical passages about how to facilitate this process. The caution with the principles, however, is they are *aspects* of being filled, not *steps* to being filled.

To you, what is the difference between *aspects* and *steps?*

Why might the Bible offer aspects rather than steps of being filled with the Spirit?

What aspects of the Holy Spirit's filling can you recall from previous study?

Experiencing the Holy Spirit can't be reduced to a series of steps. It isn't an assembly process—like putting prayer A in time slot Z! A dynamic relationship with God defies such arbitrary categorizations. Nevertheless, we aren't without biblical guidance toward the Spirit's filling.

The first aspect of being filled with the Holy Spirit is being sure you are saved. Only Christians can be filled with the Spirit (see Rom. 8:15-16). The second aspect of being filled with the Spirit involves a willingness to be filled. Being filled with the Spirit is an act of surrender.

Define *surrender.*

Why do you think surrendering is an important aspect of filling?

Many years ago, one of my mentors told me that being filled with the Spirit required "acquiescence of the heart to God." The word *acquiescence* means "passive submission, willing compliance." It's an incredibly appropriate term for this aspect. Being filled with the Spirit is a willing choice to become passive, to submit, to willingly cede control to the Spirit's influence.

Read Ephesians 5:18 again. How does this passage relate to surrender?

Are there any areas of your life you have not consciously surrendered to the Lord? If so, what are those areas?

The prospect of surrender is frightening because we must acknowledge we aren't in control of our lives. Most of us like control very much! Nevertheless, acquiescence is required for spiritual filling.

The third aspect of spiritual filling involves changing your behavior. Since the Holy Spirit entered your life at conversion, being filled with the Spirit is more about removing barriers to His flow through you than obtaining something new. This idea is captured in simple phrases in two separate but related passages in the Bible.

Read 1 Thessalonians 5:19 and write the phrase describing how the Spirit can be limited.

Read Ephesians 4:30 and write the phrase describing how the Spirit can be limited.

What do these verses imply you are able to do with the Spirit's life in you?

The Holy Spirit is alive in every believer, yet every believer has the capacity to stifle or quench His influence. The context of this warning encourages believers to maintain spiritual disciplines like prayer and responding to prophetic (or preached) messages. You stifle the Spirit when you neglect spiritual disciplines like prayer, Bible reading, and worship attendance.

Why would a neglect of these disciplines quench the Holy Spirit?

How would participating in such things encourage sensitivity to the Spirit?

The Holy Spirit's power can also be limited by your attitudes or actions. The admonition in Ephesians 4:30 is in the midst of Paul's instructions about managing anger, showing integrity at work, communicating with wholesome words, and avoiding bitterness, wrath, and slander. These everyday actions grieve the Spirit in your life. Your actions reveal who is in control of your thoughts, motives, and desires.

A final aspect of filling is accepting it by faith. When you pray for the Spirit's filling, no special feeling will necessarily wash over you. Inviting the Spirit's control is a spiritual exercise accomplished by faith. Remember, "As you have received Christ Jesus the Lord, walk in Him" (Col. 2:6). You received Jesus by faith. Submitting yourself to the Spirit's control is a continuing act of your faith.

Which of these aspects of the Spirit's filling do you most need to practice? Why?

How do you think your life would be different if you were filled with the Spirit?

Day 4 The Results of Filling

It might seem simpler if there was an "A+B=C" formula to being filled with the Spirit. But because there isn't, we can infer two things. First of all, faith is central to being filled. Believing you have His power and acting upon it is a faith-filled choice—not the result of working a formula. Secondly, the Bible is more concerned with the results of being Spirit-filled than the process—actions really do speak louder than words. The results of the Spirit's filling can be grouped in two broad categories—spiritual fruit and supernatural results.

Read each passage below. For each one, record whether it indicates spiritual fruit or supernatural results.

- Acts 4:31:
- Acts 9:18:
- Acts 11:24:
- Acts 13:11-12:
- Acts 13:52:

The fruit of the Spirit are character qualities produced by the Spirit. These aren't native to humanity or produced by natural effort. Yet they are precisely the qualities the Spirit produces in Christians. Being filled with the Spirit results in a transformed character—change produced by the Holy Spirit shaping your mind, will, and emotions so you demonstrate being "a new creation" (2 Cor. 5:17) in Jesus.

Read Galatians 5:19-23. What word did Paul use to describe the characteristics in the list prior to the fruit of the Spirit?

Why do you think he chose the word "works" for the flesh and the word "fruit" for the Spirit?

The label "fruit" communicates something passively produced by the natural process of a source expressing itself.

Read John 15:5. How does this verse relate to the fruit of the Spirit?

Jesus is in you as the indwelling Holy Spirit and your Source for spiritual fruit. Character transformation is evidence of the Spirit's filling and unexplainable except as the result of transformation by Jesus.

The results don't stop there. Other evidences of the Spirit's filling are supernatural ministry results. These may take many forms, but the outcomes most closely associated with Antioch were large numbers of converts, generous offerings, healthy conflict resolution, and the missionary advance of the gospel.

Have you ever witnessed supernatural results because of the filling of the Holy Spirit? What happened?

Do you believe such a thing might happen through you? Why or why not?

To be indwelled with the Spirit is to have Him take up residence inside of you. Therefore, seeing the miraculous emerge out of the mundane is a realistic expectation when you are filled with the Holy Spirit.

If such results can be expected when the Spirit fills individuals, can you imagine what would happen when a dozen, fifty, or even hundreds of such individuals met together regularly? That was the case at Antioch. Corporate supernatural results are the natural outworking of individuals being filled with the Spirit.

Read Ephesians 5:15-21. Focusing on verses 19-21, what specifically did Paul say would result from being filled with the Spirit?

Why do you think being filled with the Spirit would lead to corporate expressions and ministry results?

What comes to mind when you think of an entire church of people filled with the Spirit?

Day 5 A Church of Power

Since Spirit-filled individuals express their filling in a corporate atmosphere, we should expect to see the results in the church meetings at Antioch. Our model church doesn't disappoint. While the first reference to the Holy Spirit in Antioch was describing an individual (Barnabas), the other two references are in the context of worship services.

Read Acts 11:27-30. In what ways was the Holy Spirit involved in this passage?

Agabus was a speaker of some renown from the Jerusalem church (see Acts 21:10). In response to his prediction, the Antioch believers did the "Christian" thing—helping their brothers and sisters in Jerusalem with an offering. On one level, this seems like a simple relief offering, an act of love from one church family to another. But there is far more below the surface.

Think back to how Barnabas was sent to Antioch. What did the Jerusalem church think of the Antioch church?

Given that, how might the Antioch church have responded to a request for such an offering?

Remember that despite Jesus' command in Acts 1:8 for the church to expand to the entire world, it wasn't until persecution broke out that believers by and large began to leave Jerusalem. Now Agabus, a leader from the church that hoarded the gospel and even wondered whether Gentiles could become Christians, had the audacity to ask the Antioch believers for an offering! Remarkably, they gave it.

This story reveals two aspects of the Holy Spirit's work in the worship services at Antioch. Not only did He enable preaching by Agabus and receptivity among the congregation, but the Spirit also enabled generous giving.

Have you ever seen the Spirit do similar things in your congregation? When?

What separates such occasions from regular meetings?

Time passed and several men—Barnabas, Simeon, Lucius, Manaen, and Paul—emerged as a leadership team for the Antioch church. They were directing a worship service involving prayer and fasting when members of the church were prompted with an unusual message.

Read Acts 13:1-3. What was the message? Why might such a message be considered unusual?

How do you think most modern churches would have responded to such a message?

Strangely, the message came *through* the church members *to* the missionary team, demonstrating the Spirit's vitality in the congregation as a whole. As a result, this was the first time a church formally set apart workers and sent them on a mission trip. Further, these weren't "regular" members—they were the most senior leaders. This reveals the sacrificial mind-set of the Antioch church. They were willing to give their best based on the Holy Spirit's direction.

The Holy Spirit still engages in similar activities today. He still empowers speakers and energizes the preached Word of God. He still enables congregational response, including generous giving. The Spirit directs congregational decision-making, calls people to new fields of service, and sustains missionary advance by motivating churches to give up their assets for kingdom advance

Which of these occurrences would be most surprising if it occurred in your church? Why?

What attitude should believers adopt when going to church, given these examples of the Spirit's work?

In short, transformational churches experience the Holy Spirit's in their worship services. They have a *holy expectation* something will happen *every time* they gather to worship God. That doesn't mean every person has a dramatic, life-altering experience in every worship service. It does mean, however, these kinds of experiences are happening regularly in ways that can't be predicted or controlled.

Is there evidence of the Holy Spirit's work in and through your church? If so, how?

How might you play a role in creating a sense of holy expectation in your church?

SESSION 3

Advancing the Gospel

11-6-11

SESSION 3

LAY THE FOUNDATION

1. Look back at the daily devotions you completed this week. Share one particular insight that was meaningful to you with your group.

2. As you studied the aspects of spiritual filling, which one did you find you needed to pay more attention to this week?

3. What are some ways worship services would be different if everyone in your church was committed to seeking the filling of the Spirit?
   more people ; filling of spirit from His word

4. Why is spiritual power an essential element to the advancement of the gospel? Satan is in the world.

FRAME THE DISCUSSION

Watch the discussion starter on the DVD then discuss the following questions with your group.

Gospel always produces positive Results

1. What part of your community hasn't "gotten wet" yet? That is to say, is there a part of your community that is relatively untouched by the gospel?
   Affluent
2. What are some of the specific obstacles to that part of your community being reached with the gospel?
   Apathy Rejection Skeptical · Anger
3. On the scale below, mark how important you think advancing the gospel is to American Christians with 1 being not important and 10 being a must:

1 2 3 4 5 6 7 8 9 10

4. What are some of the main reasons Christians might give for neglecting to share the gospel?

Watch the teaching segment from the DVD using the viewer guide below.

Barnabas sent to Antioch. He brought Paul

Innovations at Antioch:

1. First teaching ministry among gentiles
2. First called "Christians"
3. First MISSIONARY movement

Innovation is being willing to do New things to Advance the gospel.

doing something that's never been done before

Wrong Reasons to Change:

1. To copy successful models

   We must apply PRINCIPLES not practices.

2. To make ourselves feel more comfortable

Change should be introduced to expand the gospel's WITNESS, to strengthen and ENLarge your church, and to expand and promote God's kingdom.

Do whatever it takes to make sure the church is strong, for the next generation.

Discuss the teaching segment with your group using the questions below.

1. Think about a person in your life who you believe to be committed to advancing the gospel. What characterizes his or her life? Solid foundation, sense of urgency, Bible Study + prayer + service, sacrifice, hospitality, generosity, perserverance, LORD is "NATURAL" in their conversation

2. What about a church? What characterizes a church whose priority is the advancement of the gospel?

3. Why is innovation in a church important in the advancement of the gospel?

4. What role do you have as an individual in cultivating a greater commitment in your church to gospel advancement?

Close with prayer.

FINISHING TOUCHES

Scripture Memory

> "There is salvation in no one else, for there is no other name under heaven given to people, and we must be saved by it." **Acts 4:12**

Building Antioch

- Examine your daily schedule. Are there any opportunities in which you come in regular contact with people who don't know Jesus? If not, add something to your routine with the goal of sharing the gospel with unbelievers.
- Commit to pray for one person daily who you know does not know Jesus.
- Pray that your church would become a people committed to doing whatever it takes to reach your community with the gospel.

Video sessions are available for purchase at *www.lifeway.com/buildingantioch*

SESSION 3

Advancing the Gospel

"How big a place does the gospel have in your life?" Most Christians would probably answer, "It's important but not as important as it should be." Sharing the message of God's love, demonstrated in the sacrifice of Jesus for the sin of the world, should be important to every Christian, but we get busy. We work. We shop. We go to meetings. We take our children to practices and recitals. We go to movies, watch television, and mow the lawn. We are all busy people.

For most of us, life gets in the way of advancing the gospel.

The Christians at Antioch lived a different way. For them, the gospel went beyond being a part of their lives—even beyond being the most important part of their lives. Advancing the gospel was their central passion and focus. Everything else was built around their commitment to make Jesus known in the world.

As you read their story, you sense everything in their lives, and consequently in their church, was weighed against this question: "Does this activity serve to advance the gospel?" The Christians at Antioch had little interest in pursuing any activity, relationship, priority, or aspiration that didn't contribute to that end.

Their lives were drastically and radically altered so that, in all things, they might consider the gospel first. That attitude indicates individuals who have been transformed. And transformed individuals make up transformational churches.

BUILDING
ANTIOCH

Day 1 The Gospel at Antioch

If you asked one of the first followers of Jesus where, in their opinion, the message of the gospel would be most readily accepted, it's doubtful many would have said the city of Antioch.

Antioch was a significant city, an urban capital of the Roman province where it was located. It was religiously cosmopolitan, a cult center for worshiping gods like Zeus, Poseidon, Adonis, and Tyche. Because Antioch was a port city, a transportation hub, and a governmental capital, all Greeks, Phoenicians, Jews, Arabs, Persians, and Italians lived in multicultural pluralism.

Each of these ethnic groups believed in a different god or gods. Furthermore, the Roman Empire kept the peace among its conquered peoples by allowing them to retain their gods, so long as they also worshiped the Roman emperor as supreme. To these realities, add the fact that during the early years of the Christian movement the gospel was retained largely among the Jewish community in Jerusalem. All of these factors made Antioch a seemingly unlikely location for the rapid expansion of the gospel.

But then again, God often works in ways we don't expect.

Which of the above do you think was the greatest challenge for the gospel to overcome? Why?

How are these challenges similar to contemporary challenges to advancing the gospel? How are they different?

What perspective should Christians take when confronted with challenges like these?

The spread of the gospel to Gentiles in Antioch was not without precedent. Early examples of Gentile-reaching efforts include Philip's ministry in Samaria (see Acts 8:4-13) and later with the Ethiopian eunuch (see Acts 8:26-39). God endorsed these efforts through Peter's vision and subsequent visit with Cornelius (see Acts 10). These incidents stand out as exceptions to the prevailing practice of the early church, which was sharing the gospel primarily with Jews.

Read Acts 11:19-21. How did the gospel eventually spread to Antioch?

What do you think those carriers of the gospel felt as they entered Antioch and began to share?

These anonymous men—never named in the Bible, identities lost in church history—broke the mold and began preaching the gospel openly in the Gentile community. While that seems like standard operating procedure to Christians today, at the time it was a courageous act by men who risked their lives to advance the gospel.

What risks did those preachers take to spread the gospel?

What about you? What risks would you encounter if you advanced the gospel with similar fervency?

Generations of Jewish tradition and years of early Christian practice mandated these brave men be circumspect with the gospel. Yet, they cast aside all restraint, preached the gospel to the Gentiles, "and a large number who believed turned to the Lord" (Acts 11:21).

Again, God surprised the world. The unlikeliest of people in the unlikeliest of places not only received the gospel but so committed themselves to spreading it that Antioch became a center for missionary activity. In fact, most of you reading these words are doing so as a result of the gospel coming to and through Antioch. Because of the message going to Antioch, the door opened to all Gentiles and the word of life continued to spread without prejudice.

How do you think the courage of the early preachers impacted the way believers at Antioch felt about spreading the gospel?

Who is one person who sacrificed so you might hear the gospel?

How will you change to become more intentional about sharing the gospel?

Day 2 First Antioch

Thanks to the anonymous witnesses who were willing to take a risk in Antioch, a thriving church was established there. Those who believed the truth of Jesus grew in their faith and established a community centered on the gospel. Their church never lost touch with those core truths and consistently and willingly shared them with others. In this respect, the believers at Antioch were the first to put into practice what has become normative in transformational churches today.

Read the following passages. For each, record what happened for the first time in the Antioch church:

- **Acts 11:22-26a:**
- **Acts 11:26b:**
- **Acts 13:1-2:**

What actions and attitudes do you think earned the believers at Antioch the name "Christians"?

It was at Antioch that "the disciples were first called Christians" (Acts 11:26). This was most likely a derisive term hung on the early followers of "The Way" by their critics and detractors. They ridiculed believers as the "Christ-ones," men and women who talked so often about "the Christ" they earned a new nickname.

Have you ever been around a person who fit that description? What is it like to talk with that person?

Does your behavior and dialogue with others center on Jesus to the extent that you are known as a Christian?

It's not hard to imagine how this moniker may have come about. Early Antioch believers apparently enjoyed talking about "Jesus—the Christ" all the time, in every place, with every person. They talked about Christ while shopping in the market, watching athletic events, washing clothes at the river, and working in their shops and fields. They spoke of Christ as the center of their lives, as the One who forgave them, and as the Source of new life. Christ was the focus of their worship and the reason their ethical behavior stood in such sharp contrast to that of unbelievers in their community. Truly, they were people enamored with and consumed by Christ and His presence in their lives.

What would your nickname be if it were based on the driving passion of your life?

How is this similar to or different from the attitude many of us take toward evangelism today?

Interestingly, it seems these Christians did not have a specific time set aside for the purpose of advancing the gospel. Though there may have been a time set aside for witnessing in the community, it seems such a time would have simply been an extension of what these believers were already doing anyway. They didn't wait until a designated hour on Wednesday or Sunday for outreach. Instead, they encountered Jesus in such a life-changing and powerful way they had little else to talk about than Him. Every conversation came back to the gospel.

In contrast, Jesus is seldom mentioned by many believers in any secular context today. Conversations about Jesus at work, on the ball field, while shopping, or at any other time in everyday life are rare when believers interact with unbelievers. Not in Antioch! Christ dominated their thinking and influenced their interactions to the extent that their vocabulary earned them a nickname that has since become the defining label for the movement initiated by Jesus.

Why do you think your attitude is different than the one expressed in Antioch?

How do you think you can move closer to following the example of the Antioch believers?

In Antioch, advancing the gospel was not merely an activity. It was a lifestyle. It was not something forced; it was as natural as eating or drinking. Those Christians understood Jesus had changed everything about their lives—the way they worked, the way they interacted with government officials, the way they lived in community—everything was different.

Rather than trying harder to advance the gospel, perhaps you should change your perspective on the gospel. Make living it and sharing it central to your existence. When you realize the breadth and depth of the message of Jesus, you'll understand advancing the gospel isn't just something we do; it's who we are.

Read Acts 4:19-20. How was Peter and John's answer similar to the attitude displayed in Antioch?

Pray today that you will have a greater understanding of how deeply the gospel affects you and affects a growing passion to extend the message to everyone.

Day 3 In the World

In Antioch, the gospel wasn't just shared; Christians lived it out among unbelievers. What a contrast from our experience today! Despite the abundance of evangelistic books and training programs, believers still struggle with simply sharing the good news of Jesus—much less living the gospel as a perpetual witness.

What are the three most common reasons Christians struggle with sharing the gospel?

1.

2.

3.

Which of these reasons sounds most like you?

The reasons Christians are reluctant witnesses are many and varied. Some are afraid of saying something wrong. Others are concerned about the response of the person with whom they are sharing. Still others might see sharing the gospel as overstepping the boundaries of a friendship. But perhaps another reason for our failure to advance the gospel is much simpler than all these: We don't really know anyone with whom to share it.

Increasingly, Christians seem to be forming fewer and fewer genuine relationships with non-Christians. We tend toward isolationism. As Christianity has grown, particularly in a specialized society, there are more and more opportunities for Christians to only associate with other Christians. Today, you can find Christian concerts, Christian schools, Christian sports leagues, and Christian social networking sites to enjoy—without worldly connections or interactions.

Do you see the trend toward isolationism in your life?

What is positive about that?

What is challenging about it?

Most Christian-alternative activities are initiated with noble intentions. As followers of Jesus, we are rightly concerned about being polluted by the world (see 1 John 2:15-17; Jas. 1:27). To pursue moral and ethical purity, we pick and choose carefully what cultural elements we allow into our lives and homes. However, taken too far, such guarding can turn into the kind of isolationism that prevents Christians from accomplishing their purpose in the world.

Read 1 John 2:15-17. What do you think John meant by "the world"?

What does it mean to love the world?

Read John 17:15-18. What specifically did Jesus say about the relationship between Christians and the world?

One of the biggest ways we can prioritize advancing the gospel is actively forming relationships with non-Christians. For some who work primarily with Christians in churches or ministry organizations, this requires focused intentionality. Regardless of our vocation, we are commissioned by Jesus to engage lost people and share the gospel among people who have never heard it.

In His high-priestly prayer, Jesus made specific mention of this necessity. He asked the Father *not* to remove believers from the world. Christians must be in the world, forming relationships with non-Christians, if the gospel is to spread among them.

What part of your schedule brings you into regular contact with nonbelievers?

How are you actively pursuing relationships with them?

How often do you pray for them?

Isolationism was a foreign concept to the church at Antioch. So ingrained was the call to share the gospel, they would have balked at cutting themselves off from unbelievers. The Antioch Christians didn't have the option to drive home from work and close the garage door. They interacted daily with people from all over the world, of different belief systems, in the markets, at the shops, and in the streets of their city.

Because of our specialized society, many believers have groceries delivered, rent movies online, and "friend" people electronically. We should consider whether doing those things, convenient though they may be, are symptomatic of our growing isolationism. Failure to engage unbelievers in meaningful relationships hinders the work of sharing the gospel.

What are three ways you might intentionally come into more contact with unbelievers or maximize the relationships you already have for the gospel?

1.

2.

3.

Day 4 Intentional Missionary Movement

The city of Antioch was located in present-day Turkey, about 12 miles from the Syrian border. Though Antioch was only about 300 miles from Jerusalem, the birthplace of the church and the Christian movement, there was an ocean of cultural prejudice to be crossed between the cities.

Antioch was the first predominantly Gentile church in history. Those believers were living proof of God's desire and intent the gospel should supersede every culture, language, nation, and people. God's family would be a multiethnic, multinational host of believers. The diverse believing community at Antioch is proof such congregations can exist.

What are some of the challenges to being a multicultural congregation?

How do you think the church at Antioch was able to overcome those challenges?

What is your responsibility as a Christian, given God's desire for a multicultural family?

With what group of people would you be least likely to share the gospel? Why?

Believers who have been transformed by the gospel recognize God's power to change others with the same message. A transformed person knows there is no person beyond grace, no person off-limits to the gospel. When changed people come together in a church, they follow in the footsteps of the Antioch Christians who, for the first time, came together as a sending church. Because they were once "off-limits" themselves, they realized the message of Jesus was not something to cling to selfishly. It was meant to be passed along to others. Antioch was the birthplace of the first intentional missionary movement.

Read Acts 13:1-3. Given such a task had never before been intentionally attempted, do you think such actions were difficult for the church? Why or why not?

What about today? What specific challenges stand in the way of intentional missionary efforts?

During a worship service, the Holy Spirit told the church to send Barnabas and Paul to share the gospel and start new churches in other cities. The tone of the story intimates the church responded fairly quickly to those directions and "after they had fasted, prayed, and laid hands on them, they sent them off" (Acts 13:3).

The first trip resulted in new churches in Cyprus, Pisidian Antioch, Iconium, Lystra, and Derbe. The missionary team eventually returned to Antioch. "After they ... gathered the church together, they reported everything God had done with them and that He had opened the door of faith to the Gentiles. And they spent a considerable time with the disciples" (Acts 14:27-28).

The continued support, interest, and accountability the Antioch church demonstrated for the missionary team is evident in their response to the trip-reporting service.

What are the key characteristics of being a good sending church? How did the church at Antioch demonstrate those characteristics?

What about you? What are three ways that you might become a more active sender—a person who helps the gospel go global?

The first journey wasn't the end of the mission endeavors of the church at Antioch. Eventually, Paul and Barnabas separated, ending their partnership in the gospel (see Acts 15:36-40) and apparently their relationship (as far as recorded in the Bible). Nevertheless, the Antioch church maintained its missional focus.

Read Acts 15:36-41. Where do you see that continued focus from Antioch in this passage?

How might the congregation have been tempted to respond instead?

What does their response indicate about the way they viewed gospel advancement?

When Paul and Barnabas separated, both men chose new partners (Paul chose Silas; Barnabas chose Mark). Both teams, although going separate ways, still took trips to further the mission of the gospel. Clearly, the Gentile church at Antioch had a profound, sustained commitment to spreading the gospel to other cities in the Mediterranean world. Not even a major conflict among its most beloved leaders could derail their commitment to the mission.

How different might the world be if all congregations approached the advancement of the gospel with such resolute determination! The possibilities are endless. But such corporate determination begins with individuals committing themselves to intentionality in the missionary enterprise.

What do you think are the top three priorities of your church? What makes you think that?

1.

2.

3.

Are those priorities reflective of the priorities of individuals in your church? How so?

What are some practical ways you might encourage an ever-increasing commitment to the advancement of the gospel through your church?

Day 5 Transformation and Innovation

How does a church look when its people are firmly committed to advancing the gospel? You may have never experienced such a fellowship; nevertheless, Antioch provides an encouraging model for what church life can be like.

What do you think are some of the characteristics of a church whose people are committed to the gospel?

Of the characteristics you listed, which sounds the most like your church?

How about the least? Why?

There are many characteristics that could be listed. Missional churches are generous. They are welcoming. They are loving. They are focused on the needs of others. They are willing to change. Antioch stands apart because of its commitment to innovation, constantly changing to tell more and more people about Jesus.

Antioch modeled a series of "firsts" among churches, each directly connected to the mission of advancing the gospel. They were the first predominantly Gentile congregation. They were the first to establish a teaching ministry among Gentiles. They were the first to be called "Christians." They founded the first intentional missionary movement. This church was committed to getting the gospel to more people, in more places, in whatever ways were required to be sure the church grew and the kingdom expanded.

In short, the church at Antioch was willing to change and innovate if doing so would further advance the gospel.

What was the last big change made in your church?

How did the people respond? Why?

Do you think a willingness to change is important for a transformational church? Why or why not?

Many well-meaning Christians want their church to remain just like it is. When a church begins to change, or even when pastors start talking about making significant changes, the comfort level among the membership often declines.

Churches don't need to change for the sake of change. That's not why changes were made at Antioch. Their innovations all had a singular focus, as do healthy churches today. They changed, as needed, to continually reach more and more people with the gospel. Transformational churches today refuse to settle for less than missional effectiveness and make whatever changes are necessary to ensure the gospel's progress.

If change is integral for gospel advancement, why do so many Christians struggle with it?

What truth have you learned from Antioch that will help you embrace change?

In order to embrace change for the sake of the gospel, Christians must be willing to put aside their personal preferences for the sake of others. In doing this, we adopt and demonstrate the same attitude as Jesus.

Read Philippians 2:3-11. What does this passage have to do with preferences among Christians?

How does putting others first for the sake of the gospel mirror the attitude of Jesus?

Churches committed to the advancement of the gospel rarely ask the question, "What do we like?" about issues such as music, programming, preaching style, or organization. Instead, like the church at Antioch, they are consistently looking outward rather than inward. The better question becomes, "What is the most effective way to reach more and more people with the gospel?"

Think through some specific areas of ministry in your church. For each, list one way you might encourage your church to put the gospel ahead of personal preference:

- o **Worship Ministry:**
- o **Children's Ministry:**
- o **Youth Ministry:**
- o **Men's/Women's Ministry:**
- o **Sunday School/Small Groups:**

SESSION 4

Commitment to the Truth

SESSION 4

LAY THE FOUNDATION

1. Look back at the daily devotions you completed this week. Share one particular insight that was meaningful to you with your group.

2. What are some things that might take precedence over the advancement of the gospel in the 21st century church?

3. How, specifically, did the Antioch church live out their commitment to advance the gospel?

4. What is the church's responsibility to someone after that person has accepted Christ as Savior and Lord?

FRAME THE DISCUSSION

Watch the discussion starter on the DVD then discuss the following questions with your group.

1. How is your church carrying on this legacy? How are you doing at making disciples for Jesus?

2. Define *disciple*.

3. What's the difference between a *disciple* and a *convert?*

4. Read Matthew 28:18-20. Why do you think Jesus commanded His followers to make disciples and not converts?

Watch the teaching segment from the DVD using the viewer guide below.

The goal for every church member is ________________ ________________.

All of the examples in the Bible used to describe the church reference progress, growth, and change.

Having the MIND of CHRIST is the goal for every believer in a transformational church.

Learn God's ways

The transformational church has a responsibility through its teaching ministry to help people be transformed in their beliefs and in their behaviors.

2 Corin 10:4-5

The Curriculum of Antioch:

1. The Gospel (Acts 15)
2. Finances (Acts 11:29)
3. Worship (Acts 13:2-3)
4. Missions (Acts 13:3)
5. Problem-solving skills (Acts 15:36-41)

Disciple-making churches make a significant differences in the lives of their members.

Discuss the teaching segment with your group using the questions below.

1. What is the biggest way your life has changed since you came to know Christ? A purpose & plan
   Trust in Christ | Peace | Desire to Know Bible | forgiveness
2. Did the church play a role in that change? How?
   Yes
3. Look back at the curriculum of Antioch explained in the teaching video. Which of the five aspects outlined stands out most to you? Why?
   Problem solving skills | Unity

4. Why would these five aspects be important to becoming a disciple?
5. What other essentials for discipleship in the 21st century would you add to this list?

Close with prayer.

FINISHING TOUCHES

Scripture Memory

> "Do not be conformed to this age, but be transformed by the renewing of your mind, so that you may discern what is the good, pleasing, and perfect will of God." **Romans 12:2**

Building Antioch

Evaluate your own commitment to discipleship through your church. Of what opportunities do you need to take full advantage? Come up with some specific action to that end, for example:

- Commit to teach a children's or youth Sunday School class.
- Bring a journal to worship so you can take notes.
- Join with others in your church and read through the Bible in a year.
- Set up a meeting with someone in your church you know is seeking to grow in Christ. Before you go, pray that the Lord would help you encourage that person in their pursuit of discipleship.
- Pray that your church would be committed to making disciples, not just converts.

Video sessions are available for purchase at *www.lifeway.com/buildingantioch*

SESSION 4

Commitment to the Truth

A commitment to truth is based on an unpopular assumption in our culture. To be committed to truth, we must first assume there is such a thing as absolute truth. As Christians, we believe truth is not dependent on time, place, or opinion. Truth is revealed by God and recorded in Scripture.

But in today's world, where tolerance is prized above all else, claiming truth as foundational to your belief system is viewed as supremely arrogant. Yet undeniably, that's exactly what Christians say—except with humility, not pride. Jesus is an exclusive Savior—not one way to God but *the* way to God. Likewise, the Bible isn't one holy book among many but the single and unique inspired Word of God.

The Antioch believers understood the truth about the gospel. Consequently, they were the first Gentile church to adopt a sustained teaching ministry. Coming from their various religious backgrounds and desiring lives built on truth, Antioch believers recognized the need for regular doctrinal and theological education. The same thing is needed today.

How can today's Christians walk the road of godliness? How can they know where to stand on difficult issues of cultural relevance? How can they express those views in a clear and articulate way to those around them? All these questions are answered through a commitment to truth in individuals and churches.

This is, after all, exactly how God designed the church. As a transformational community, the church welcomes sinners, assimilates new believers as members, and shapes them into fully devoted Jesus-followers.

The church stands for truth and trains Christians to live under its authority.

Make Disciples

Read Matthew 28:18-20. If you were to divide the Great Commission into parts, which do you tend to emphasize? Authority? Going? Making disciples? Baptizing? Why?

Which do you think is most emphasized in your church?

Because English translations often put "Go" at the beginning of verse 19, usually capitalized and set apart with a comma, readers incorrectly assume the emphasis is on "going." This interpretation is strengthened by our evangelical propensity for missions and evangelism. We know we should be "going," so we emphasize this aspect of Jesus' instructions. But the linguistic emphasis in this passage is on "making disciples," not "going." To capture the appropriate emphasis, consider this slight adjustment to the above translation: "Go, therefore, and *make disciples"* (emphasis added). Understanding the Great Commission like this will help us keep the emphasis straight.

What is the difference between making disciples and converting the lost?

Why do you think Jesus commanded disciple making rather than converting?

Despite this emphasis, many Christians are falling short of the standard of biblical discipleship. As a whole, the beliefs and behaviors of American believers aren't much different than their secular counterparts. The church looks a lot like the world. The church at Antioch, however, saw the importance of moving past conversion into the disciple-making process.

What were the three most pivotal insights you learned shortly after your conversion that have shaped your life as a disciple?

1.

2.

3.

When the church at Antioch started, it was almost entirely through conversion growth because itinerant preachers first shared the gospel with Gentiles. As the church formed, the only experienced leaders were the church planters. There were probably very few new believers in Antioch with much biblical background or a biblical worldview. While there was a Jewish community in Antioch, the early believers were Gentiles who most likely had little knowledge of the Old Testament. The church started with converts who had limited biblical knowledge and a secular worldview. If they did have a spiritual perspective prior to conversion (which was likely given the religious pluralism of the city), then it certainly wasn't a Christian outlook.

Read Acts 11:19-26. How committed was Barnabas to the process of discipleship? How do you know?

How might the story of Antioch have been different if Barnabas would have been content to rejoice a church had started there but then left?

Upon arriving at Antioch, Barnabas realized two things—he needed a strategy to solidify the church and he needed help to accomplish it. To solve the problem, he took an unusual step—he left town for a few days! Barnabas went about 85 miles to find Paul in Tarsus. Then these two men led an intentional and continuous teaching ministry in Antioch. The continual stream of new believers coming into the church was met with regular, systematic, thorough, and repetitive teaching. The early converts were turned into disciples.

Imagine how different the story at Antioch might have been without this kind of dedication to the truth of God's Word. It's likely the church would not have sustained later attacks of persecution and false teaching. Certainly their commitment to spreading the gospel would have been compromised, for they would not have been established in the truth of the gospel. Because of the love of truth displayed in the leadership and in the church, the believers at Antioch had a very different story.

What are the main challenges in your community to your commitment to the truth of the gospel?

What are some practical ways you might foster a greater commitment to that truth in your life? In your church?

Day 2 What is a Disciple?

Jesus' command to make disciples of all peoples was a real possibility in the city of Antioch. As a cosmopolitan melting pot of various cultures, the nations were at the doorstep of the church. Based on the account from Acts, the church was concerned about making sure their new converts were brought along in the process of discipleship.

Read the following passages. For each passage, record how it demonstrates the church's commitment to making disciples.

- Acts 13:1:
- Acts 15:32:
- Acts 15:35:

These passages all involve teaching. Is teaching the only way discipleship is accomplished? Why or why not?

What role does teaching play in the discipling process?

The primary means the church uses to develop disciples is teaching. Teaching shapes the mind. As new thoughts emerge, new attitudes and actions result. Paul amplified these ideas when he wrote, "The weapons of our warfare are not worldly, but are powerful through God for the demolition of strongholds. We demolish arguments and every high-minded thing that is raised up against the knowledge of God" (2 Cor. 10:4-5).

What does this passage say about the act of teaching?

What is the end result of good teaching?

Spiritual growth is rooted in changed thinking. Carnal thought patterns, the strongholds of "arguments and every high-minded thing that is raised up against the knowledge of God," naturally dominate the minds of unbelievers and new believers. It takes time to undo years of wrong thinking while learning God's Word and ways, how to think biblically, and how to behave accordingly. The best word to describe this process is *transformation.*

Read Matthew 5:21-22,27-28,31-34,38-39,43-44. Fill in the blanks below with what those verses all have in common:

"________ have heard that it ________ ____________ ...
But ____ tell ________ ..."

How does the pattern in Jesus' teaching reflect the reeducation necessary for changed thinking?

Jesus recognized transformation was rooted in the mind—in thought patterns that lead to behavioral changes. Accordingly, He presented a dramatic contrast in His teaching of what His audience thought to be true and what was actually true. It was through this process of reeducation that Jesus brought about transformation.

The theological word for this transformation is *sanctification.*

Sanctification literally means, "to make holy," but the doctrine of sanctification broadly encompasses all aspects of spiritual transformation. While *justification* describes your once-in-a-moment conversion experience, *sanctification* involves a lifetime of spiritual growth, change, and development. Sanctification is becoming more like Jesus, God's process of every believer being "conformed to the image of His Son" (Rom. 8:29).

Read Romans 12:1-2. How can you know what is God's will, according to this passage?

How do you think a person's mind is renewed?

Paul admonished believers to "not be conformed to this age, but be transformed by the renewing of your mind, so that you may discern what is the good, pleasing, and perfect will of God" (Rom. 12:2). The mind is renewed through new information—biblical truth—producing the enlightenment necessary for God-honoring choices. Through this process, a believer develops "the mind of Christ" (1 Cor. 2:16) or the capacity to consider, reason, and understand life from a biblical perspective or worldview.

This type of transformation—a renewed mind producing new choices based on an ingrained biblical worldview—should be the standard for every Christian.

Is there anything you are feeding into your mind that might hinder that kind of transformation?

Are you actively encouraging others in your church to renew their minds? How?

To Cut or Not to Cut

Individuals and churches are often tempted to soften their spiritual positions on certain matters, or at least mute their intensity, to become less offensive to others who disagree with those stances. That effort, even if well-intended, is a misapplication of Paul's example of becoming "all things to all people, so that I may by every possible means save some" (1 Cor. 9:22).

Read the verse above again. What do you think Paul meant by becoming "all things to all people"?

What are some specific areas of Christian belief that are the most tempting to soften or compromise? Why?

In Antioch, Paul broke new ground in contextualizing the gospel's presentation without compromising its message. On the contrary, he undertook extreme measures to defend its purity.

Christians who are committed to truth aren't afraid to declare it as revealed in Scripture and call people to submit to its authority. Unfortunately, some believers equate this responsibility with mean-spirited, aggressive, arrogant behavior. Standing for truth can—and should—be done while still showing the fruit of the Spirit. Holding strong convictions is possible—intensely, yet without compromise—while practicing humility produced by quiet confidence in the truth of Scripture. The Antioch church and its leaders modeled this balance.

Why do you think such a balance of conviction and humility is so difficult to maintain?

The first great doctrinal challenge faced by the church in Antioch was the nature of the gospel. The root of the problem was the wrong assumption by some Jewish Christians that the gospel had to remain connected to their community. In other words, they believed converts from non-Jewish backgrounds had to become Jewish in order to become Christians. The defining issue was circumcision—requiring a man to undergo this outward act, along with placing faith in Jesus for salvation, to become part of the Christian community.

Read Genesis 17:1,10-11. What was the purpose of circumcision?

Why do you think so many Jewish believers considered it a necessary step in becoming a Christian?

Is there anything similar to circumcision today, an additional action imposed on the process of conversion? If so, what?

In Antioch, the gospel had spread rapidly among Gentiles for the first time. Barnabas was dispatched to check out this new phenomenon. When Barnabas endorsed the Antioch church as God's work, the stage was set for a major conflict between Jewish believers and Gentile believers over the nature of the gospel.

Read Acts 15:1-12. Where do you see a commitment to the truth in this passage?

Paul and Barnabas were skilled speakers, experienced teachers, and much-loved pastors defending their Gentile flock. "Serious argument and debate" (Acts 15:2) indicates an intense public confrontation as rival teachers declared differing convictions about the gospel. That was really what was at stake here. The issue, fundamentally, was the means by which someone is saved. Was it by grace through faith? Or was it something else? On this issue, no compromise was possible.

The church at Antioch demonstrated their commitment to truth by providing the means for Paul and Barnabas to take their message back to the Jerusalem church where a pivotal decision in church history was made.

Read Acts 15:22-29. What was the basic message of the letter to the Gentile Christians? What was the lasting significance of that letter?

This came at a crossroads moment for the nascent Christian movement. The intensity of the debate, the arduous travel required for meetings about the issue, the high-level leaders involved, and the breadth of congregational participation by two significant churches underscored the importance of the debate at that time and for the church for all time.

The overarching lesson we learn from this story is that some convictions are worth fighting for. Just as in the case of Antioch, sometimes Christians simply must stand up and be counted.

In what ways might you encourage your church to have an ever-growing love and commitment to the truth?

Day 4 The Essential and the Important

Circumcision was the pivotal issue for deciding the church's commitment to salvation by grace through faith alone. Because of their commitment to truth, early believers preserved the gospel and centuries of future Christians have been the beneficiaries. Sometimes, the stakes are so high, doctrine must be defended no matter the personal cost.

When a core Christian doctrine is taught erroneously, the perpetrators must be called to account, challenged to repent, resisted if they won't recant their position, and dismissed (or abandoned) if necessary. You have biblical permission, even an obligation, to defend key doctrinal issues to this extreme.

There's no doubt, rejecting circumcision as part of the gospel was a hill worth dying on, an essential point of doctrinal conviction to be defended at all cost. In an effort to defend appropriate doctrines, however, we must also recognize not every issue is of such importance.

What doctrinal issues would you define as "essential"?

Which are important but not essential? Why is it important to know the difference?

There are times when compromise is appropriate to preserve fellowship with other believers. As a worldwide movement, Christianity is too complex to define one single "Christian way" for every life issue in all contexts. Cultural influences on Christianity create permissible variety among genuine believers in areas like political persuasions, worship methods, food choices, family relationships, and preaching styles.

Paul, the same man who aggressively opposed circumcision as part of the gospel, soon demonstrated a remarkable deference to cultural practices on this same issue.

Read Acts 16:1-5. In your own words, what happened in this story?

What is strange about Paul's treatment of Timothy?

Why do you think Paul acted in this manner?

Paul, who had just fought and won a pitched battle against circumcision, immediately started his next missionary journey by circumcising a young leader before allowing him to join the missionary team. The reason for Paul's decision was "because of the Jews who were in those places, since they all knew that his father was a Greek" (Acts 16:3).

Though Paul refused to circumcise anyone as part of their conversion experience (thus preserving the gospel), he circumcised a protégé in order to remove barriers to missional and ministerial effectiveness. This wasn't a repudiation of his former position because, after the circumcision, Paul and Timothy went forth to deliver the news from the Jerusalem elders. Ironically, Paul circumcised Timothy so that they could more freely preach a circumcision-less gospel.

How do you personally know the difference between an important and an essential doctrine?

If a doctrine is important but not essential, how do you appropriately stand for the truth?

There are certain doctrines that define the Christian faith. They are the core of what we believe. When a person denies one of these, they deny the faith. Doctrines of God (including Father, Son, and Spirit), Salvation, and Scripture fall into this category.

But how do you know if something goes in this category? Without being flippant, the answer is that these are doctrines worth dying for. This is a reality to many believers around the world who face persecution. Some truth is worth dying for and some isn't! Knowing the difference is vital to successfully defend the faith while avoiding pointless legalistic arguments over lesser issues.

Read Romans 14:13-23. List some of the principles Paul advised in determining how to deal with lesser issues.

Is there an overriding principle to which we should submit ourselves? What is it?

In the case of circumcision, Paul refused to act out of pride. He might have chosen to not circumcise Timothy to make a point or demonstrate his unbending stance. But Paul instead chose to be ruled by his love of the gospel and those in need of it, rather than legalism about an optional practice. A good question to ask when confronted with a similar issue is, "What decision would promote the good of others and the advancement of the gospel?"

Oh, that this was a simple, clean, conflict-free process! But it isn't. It's messy, troublesome, and complicated. Yet the stakes are high. The unity of the church and the nature of the gospel are at stake.

Are there issues you are currently encountering that should be considered important rather than essential? If so, list them.

Are there issues you have compromised that you should have considered essential? If so, list them.

What are some practical ways you might choose to promote unity in the church over such issues?

Day 5 A Church for the Truth

When believers are committed to truth, both in learning and teaching, what are the effects on the church? What are the effects on the community in which that church is located?

These are questions that can be asked of Antioch. What was the result there? Did teaching in Antioch produce transformation? Did life change result? Did the disciple-making efforts of Paul, Barnabas, and other teachers and guest preachers facilitate changed attitudes and behaviors? There is clear evidence in Acts in the affirmative, and these same areas are still paramount for believers today.

What are three words you think of when considering a church committed to the truth?

1.

2.

3.

How do you think such a church is perceived in its community?

Teaching the gospel, along with its implications and applications, changed lives in Antioch. From the fallow ground of Gentile secularism, a vibrant church emerged in a relatively short time. Men and women who had no Christian background and little prior exposure to a biblical worldview were soon demonstrating the wisdom and character of Jesus in decisions and actions.

In both Antioch and churches today, one key area that this applied teaching is evident is in a transformed understanding of financial resources.

Read Acts 11:27-30. What need was presented to the church at Antioch? What does their response tell you about their beliefs?

How does that passage show us an example of transformation as a result of commitment to the truth?

Early Christians and churches were often poor. There's no reason to believe Antioch was any different. Yet, when offered the opportunity to give to famine relief, they did so willingly and generously. Each one gave "according to his ability" (Acts 11:29), indicating personal transformation had occurred. More than a corporate gift given from previously pooled resources, this gift was an offering given by individuals. Being taught Christian stewardship probably established the foundation for this offering.

Transformation is also evident in the church's value of and participation in corporate worship services.

Read Acts 11:27-30; 13:2-3. How was transformation visible in these corporate worship experiences?

Previously, these Gentiles may have participated in all manner of cultic worship practices—involving everything from animal sacrifice to sexual debauchery. Through its teaching ministry, the Antioch church developed worship practices that included hearing and responding to preaching, giving offerings, prayer, fasting, discerning the Holy Spirit's leading, and commissioning missionaries through laying on hands.

How was transformation visible in the act of setting apart Paul and Barnabas for service in Acts 13:2-3?

What beliefs established through teaching might have contributed to such an action?

The Antioch believers progressed from being an object of missionary outreach to a church sending missionaries—while still first-generation believers. That's rapid progress! Related to this is the personal transformation of individuals into witnesses. This resulted in the title of "Christian" first being used in Antioch. Their transformation, and resulting public witness, was so profound it earned them a derisive nickname they wore with pride.

By any measure, the Antioch church is a model of transformation. Through its teaching ministry, in obedience to Jesus' instructions, true disciples were made in Antioch. Doctrinal convictions were established, stewardship was learned and practiced, Christian worship was celebrated, and witnessing and missionary outreach flourished. This church stands apart as an example of a church making disciples—men and women renewing their minds and learning to act more and more like Jesus.

Look back at the evidences of transformation in Antioch listed above. How would you evaluate your church on this basis?

What are some specific ways you might encourage a commitment to truth which would lead to such evidences of transformation in your church?

SESSION 5

Generous Sacrifice

SESSION 5

LAY THE FOUNDATION

1. Look back at the daily devotions you completed this week. Share one particular insight that was meaningful to you with your group.

2. How specifically did you see the church at Antioch express its commitment to the truth?

3. Do you think most of us have similar commitments to the truth? How do you know?

4. What are some essential elements of faith that we must not compromise?

FRAME THE DISCUSSION

Watch the discussion starter on the DVD then discuss the following questions with your group.

1. How much is enough?

2. What are some reasons God might be concerned about the generosity of His people?

3. What's the difference between a person who practices generosity and a generous person? Is this distinction important to make? Why or why not?

4. Is generosity strictly financial? What other areas of life might a spirit of generosity affect?

Watch the teaching segment from the DVD using the viewer guide below.

Luke 6:38 9:10-11

God blesses generous Christians and generous churches.

The church at Antioch gave out of CONVICTION because they had a passion for getting the gospel to the nations.

Transformational churches overcome excuses and make a generous commitment to giving away their resources.

Generosity at Antioch

1. Gave to meet human needs

2. Supported missions and ____________________

   No matter what size your church, you have a ____________________ and an ____________________ to be generous in giving to missions and missionaries.

3. Shared their most capable ________________

Churches reflect the generosity of their members.

In the United States, evangelical Christians give an average of just less than 3 % of their annual income to God's work.

Discuss the teaching segment with your group using the questions below.

1. Read Luke 6:38. Share with your group a specific instance when you have seen this verse played out in your own life.

2. What sorts of things might keep individuals from being generous with their resources?

   WORRY

3. What about churches? Why might churches not be generous with their resources?

4. Why do you think generosity is an important characteristic for transformational churches?

5. How would a community change if a church was truly committed to generosity?

Close with prayer.

FINISHING TOUCHES

Scripture Memory

> "The One who provides seed for the sower and bread for food will provide and multiply your seed and increase the harvest of your righteousness. You will be enriched in every way for all generosity, which produces thanksgiving to God through us."
> **2 Corinthians 9:10-11**

Building Antioch

- Keep a journal this week to record every expenditure. At the end of the week, evaluate your generosity. What changes might you need to make to free up more money to give away?
- Carry an extra $10 in your pocket this week. Ask the Lord to give you an opportunity to buy someone's lunch, pay for someone's groceries, or provide some other random act of kindness.
- Pray that your church would move more and more to being a church characterized by generosity.

Video sessions are available for purchase at *www.lifeway.com/buildingantioch*

SESSION 5

Generous Sacrifice

Jesus said, "Give, and it will be given to you; a good measure—pressed down, shaken together, and running over—will be poured into your lap. For with the measure you use, it will be measured back to you" (Luke 6:38).

While Jesus made that promise in the context of granting and receiving forgiveness, the principle has broader application. Jesus used the analogy of a basket being filled with grain—a good measure. When it seemed full, the grain could be pressed down and shaken together, thus increasing the amount the basket could hold. Jesus taught that generous givers will be replenished like that grain basket. They will have so much their container will run over!

Generous sacrifice is a mark of transformed people. They give themselves away. They give when they are struggling financially as well as when they have plenty. They give out of conviction—believing God will honor them for their generosity and meet any needs created by their giving.

The Antioch believers modeled generosity. Their compassion for others and passion for spreading the gospel were expressed in tangible gifts—of money and people—that still serve as examples for us today.

BUILDING **ANTIOCH**

Day 1 Rich Stewards

The characteristic of generous sacrifice stands in stark contrast to the prevailing attitude of many in our culture. In all areas, we are encouraged to get more for ourselves. Whether it's money, position, influence, or possessions, people want more. The concept of "enough" is not common in our world.

That might be the economic perspective of the world around us, but in the kingdom of God, the attitude is far different. In His kingdom, joy is found in giving rather than receiving. We don't work just to buy a bigger house or build a healthy retirement fund. We work not only to meet our needs but also to earn resources to help others. The question in God's kingdom is not how much we acquire and hoard but how much we invest in others.

Given our bent toward accumulation, you might wonder if it's possible for a Christian to truly live generously. It is. Joyfully so, in fact. The beginning of such an attitude is the recognition of a very simple but profound principle illustrated by a parable in Matthew 25.

Read Matthew 25:14-30. Note who or what each of the following parts of the parable represents:

- **The rich man:**
- **The slaves:**
- **The talents:**

Is there anything surprising about this parable to you? If so, what is it?

Try and sum up Jesus' point by telling this story in one sentence below.

The parable of the talents, as it has come to be known, was told by Jesus as part of a series of stories explaining specific principles about the end of the age. With these stories, Jesus explained to His disciples what they might expect after His resurrection and how they were to live in the time between when He would ascend to heaven and return once again.

Jesus, like the rich man in the story, was going away for a while. In His absence, He has entrusted His servants, or disciples, with the responsibility of managing His affairs. It is quite a responsibility, as illustrated in this story. The word "talent" might not mean much to us, but the money described in this passage was substantial. If converted to modern terms, this man left his servants almost two million dollars between them to manage.[1]

In the story, who was the owner of the talents? What were the slaves, in relation to the talents?

How do you think the fact that the slaves were not the true owners of the talents changed the way they viewed the money?

What are three implications this parable has for the way we live?

1.

2.

3.

This parable of the kingdom points out the privilege Christians have between the time of Jesus' ascension and His second coming. Like the men in the story, we have been entrusted with vast resources. Time, intellect, financial capability, spiritual gifts—the list could go on and on. That doesn't even mention the one area where we are the most blessed. We are rich in the knowledge of the gospel.

But we do not *own* these things—not one of them. Not one minute. Not one dollar. They have all been entrusted to us as stewards. As such, it's our responsibility to make the most of what we have been given to manage. If we truly believe the Owner of these resources is coming back and we are only caretakers of those resources, then we must be actively, intentionally, and radically generous with them. We must be givers if we are to hear, "Well done, good and faithful servants" (see Matt. 25:23).

Alternatively, we can—like the man in the story—take what we have been entrusted with and bury it in the ground. We can be hoarders, not making the most of what we have been given. Jesus talked about the stewards who choose that option, too.

What, in your mind, is the key difference between the behavior of an owner and a steward?

Is there anything in your life you are treating as if you are an owner rather than a steward?

Day 2 Blessed to be a Blessing

In a relatively short period of time, the Antioch believers had progressed from new converts to sacrificial givers. How did this happen? There is no detailed answer in Acts, but there are hints about how the process might have unfolded. Paul and Barnabas taught the church "for a whole year" (Acts 11:26). No curriculum is described or prescribed. Possible content of their teaching can be surmised, however, from later events recorded in Acts.

List a few issues you think Paul and Barnabas might have considered "the basics" of Christianity to teach the church at Antioch.

Was stewardship on your list? Why or why not?

Is there much talk of stewardship in your church? Why or why not?

Paul and Barnabas must have taught the gospel, its implications, and its nuances. They taught the new believers how to distinguish doctrinal error and stand for truth. That's clear from the support the Antioch church gave them in opposition to the proponents of circumcision. They probably taught about a church's responsibility to spread the gospel—hence, the genesis of the church planting movement through Antioch. Instruction, not spontaneous insight, made these realities part of their newfound Christian faith. Based on their sacrificial giving, stewardship was evidently also a part of those early lessons.

What would be the benefit of teaching stewardship lessons early in the spiritual life of a Christian?

Perhaps Paul and Barnabas pointed the new believers to the direct teaching of Jesus on the matter of money. Maybe they taught them the biblical concept of tithing—giving 10 percent of one's gross income for kingdom purposes. Based on their disciplined giving, with each giving "according to his ability" (Acts 11:29), the disciples at Antioch learned such lessons of proportional giving. Perhaps the teachers pointed the new believers all the way back to the days of Abram, and through his story, taught a lesson about God's purpose in blessing His people.

Read the call of Abram in Genesis 12:1-3. Using the chart below, write the responsibilities of Abram and what God promised to do in and through him.

Abram's Responsibility	God's Blessing

The call itself required a great deal of faith on Abram's part. God told him to go but didn't tell him where. Furthermore, though the Lord told him he would be the father of a great many descendants, Abram was very old and childless. Despite these obstacles, God made incredible promises of blessing "all the peoples on earth" through him (Gen. 12:3).

In this call, Abram (renamed "Abraham" in Gen. 17) became the father of the Jewish nation. The words of the Lord recorded here are foundational for the people of God. They reveal God's people, starting with Abram, were going to be special recipients of blessings through the ages. But they were not blessed so they might be comfortable, hoarding those blessings from God.

According to this passage, why were Abraham and his descendants blessed? Who would be the ultimate beneficiaries of that blessing?

What bearing does this story have on our understanding of stewardship?

The New Testament reveals the true children of Abraham are those who believe as he did. That means every believer, including those in Antioch, becomes part of the line of Abraham, regardless of their physical lineage. As such, we share in this initial call to be a blessing to others.

The people of God are blessed in all sorts of ways. We are blessed materially, intellectually, and relationally. Most of all, we are blessed with the knowledge of Jesus Christ and the gospel. We have not been blessed for our sake but for the sake of others. We have been blessed to be a blessing.

Read Psalm 67. How does this passage relate to Genesis 12?

Are you more prone to hoard blessings or pass them along? Why?

What is one blessing from God you are currently hoarding? What are some specific ways you might become a blessing to others?

Day 3 Giving Away Money

Many pastors are afraid to talk about money-related issues. They fear offending people, particularly non-Christians, who hear them speak on these subjects. Such messages are desperately needed however. Greed is rampant in the American church. Most surveys indicate American evangelicals only give about 3 percent—yes only *3 percent*—of their income to support kingdom endeavors.

In addition, if we want to be biblically faithful, we must recognize money was one of Jesus' favorite sermon topics.

Read Matthew 6:19-24. Sum up Jesus' teaching in this passage in one sentence.

According to Jesus, what is the deeper issue behind our relationship with money?

It's not that God is a beggar in need of spare change to complete His directives. Rather, Jesus taught that your checkbook is often the best indicator of the state of your heart, and the heart is what concerns Him. The church at Antioch revealed their spiritual devotion time and time again in their generosity.

Read Acts 11:27-30. What message did Agabus deliver to the church?

How did the church respond?

How do you think you would have responded, if you were in a similar situation?

Agabus was a well-known preacher in the early church, and his message to Antioch was simple: Famine was coming and relief funds were needed in Judea. When the church heard this message, they immediately responded generously. This seems like such a simple story ... until you consider the background.

The context for the offering is significant. The Jerusalem church had been given the gospel and told to share it with the whole world (see Acts 1:8). They had experienced Pentecost; the inauguration of the gospel movement evidenced by believers speaking in multiple languages (see Acts 2:1-4). Despite these clear instructions and supernatural interventions, the Jerusalem church did *not* aggressively share the gospel among the Gentiles. For several years after Pentecost, the church kept the gospel in Jerusalem.

When the gospel finally exploded from its Jerusalem-imposed shackles, it did so only as a result of persecution and the forced scattering of believers (see Acts 8:4; 11:19).

Given these circumstances, how might the Antioch Christians have responded to an appeal for funds?

How do think your church would respond? How do you know?

Imagine if a church from another denomination attacked your church, questioned your faith, publicly criticized your ministry efforts ... and then sent one of their pastors to ask you for an offering to help them recover from a natural disaster.

While some churches might resist giving in these circumstances, the Antioch church did not. They sent money to the famine victims, not holding their previous behavior against them. Hungry people needed help. That fact trumped everything. The willing generosity of the Antioch Christians is a remarkable story of love overcoming divisions among believers to meet a pressing need.

At Antioch, "each of the disciples, according to his ability, determined to send relief to the brothers who lived in Judea" (Acts 11:29). This offering wasn't given out of the surplus of a few wealthy members. Nor was it made from previously collected funds available in the church. It was a widespread effort of shared sacrifice. The Antioch Christians gave according to their ability or in proportion to their resources. Generous churches are made up of individuals willing to sacrifice so their church can, in turn, make a corporate impact with its giving.

Read 2 Corinthians 9:7. Is your giving more often cheerful or out of obligation? Why?

Why do you think God loves a cheerful giver?

What does cheerful giving indicate about your beliefs?

Day 4 Giving Away Leaders

Most Christians expect their church to be generous with its money. They expect their church to use its financial resources to build its ministry and also bless others. Giving away money is one way a church demonstrates generosity. The Antioch church gave away its money. But the church also gave away something far more valuable: its best leaders.

Read Acts 13:2-3. What strikes you as unusual in this passage?

How do you think a situation like that would be handled in most churches today? Why?

Why would such a decision be difficult for the church at Antioch in particular, based on what you've learned about that church so far?

The believers gathered for worship at Antioch in a service that would change their world and ours. Barnabas, Paul, Simeon, Lucius, and Manaen—their "prophets and teachers" (Acts 13:1)—were directing the service when the Holy Spirit intervened with unusual directions: Send Barnabas and Paul as missionaries to other places. We usually think of God's call coming directly to its recipients. While that is a common pattern, it wasn't the case in this worship service. Note carefully the text, "The Holy Spirit said, 'Set apart for Me Barnabas and Saul.' " The Spirit prompted fellow believers to tell Barnabas and Paul they were being called to missionary service.

Is there room in your personal devotional life to hear the Holy Spirit speak? How can you hear His voice more readily?

How about in your church's worship services? How do you know?

The service at Antioch might have unfolded like this. A person stood up during the worship gathering and said, "I have an unusual idea. I think it's from the Lord. Paul and Barnabas, you are supposed to leave us and take the gospel to other Gentile cities." Then another person said, "That's the same impression I'm having." A third spoke up, "You won't believe this, but those thoughts have also come to my mind. I was praying just now if I should speak up." It may not have happened exactly like that, but then again, it might have! That kind of congregational participation is implied in the text. No recipient of the message is identified—only the Source is identified and emphasized. The Spirit gave Paul and Barnabas a third-party call to missions.

Why do you think the Holy Spirit chose to work in this way in Antioch?

What are some of the implications of the Holy Spirit working like this?

Churches today are usually willing to send members on mission trips or short-term assignments to neighboring congregations. They encourage youth groups to make these trips and young ministers to answer these calls. They don't usually assume, however, their senior leaders will be the first to go. Not the Antioch church. They determined to start a significant missionary movement by sending their most experienced leaders to do the job. Their generosity in sending their best leaders is another example of their willingness to give whatever was required to meet the opportunities God presented.

Which do you think was a greater sacrifice for Antioch: its money or its leaders? Why?

Did their sacrifice of leaders receive a good return? How do you know?

What would have been different if the Antioch church wasn't so generous with all resources, including leaders?

The results of their generosity were dramatic. God fulfilled His promise to bless a generous church with overflowing results. New churches were born. Preaching points on the trip allowed more people to hear the gospel and even more unnamed churches were undoubtedly started. The influence of the Antioch gift of their best leaders resulted in the gospel spreading across the Mediterranean world, churches being started in major cities, the

Christian movement gaining an irrevocable foothold among Gentiles (and still flourishing today), and the framework for the Pauline epistles, which were written to instruct those early churches, being established.

Jesus' promise of "a good measure—pressed down, shaken together, and running over" (Luke 6:38) was fulfilled through Antioch. Their generosity cemented their preeminence in church history as the model church for maximum missional impact. Their basket has certainly overflowed!

Beyond money, with what other resources in your life can you be generous?

With which of these resources would it be the most difficult for you to be generous? Why?

Ask God, right now, for an overarching spirit of generosity in all areas of your life.

Day 5 How Much?

Stewardship is a continuing, core component of discipleship. A disciple understands that systematic, routine giving is necessary for their personal edification, not only for the benefit of the church and world.

How does systematic, routine giving benefit the church and world at large? How might it benefit the giver?

Have you personally experienced such benefits?

Systematic giving is a continual reminder that everything we have belongs to God, and we possess everything temporarily. Our money and possessions are not just ours so we can be more comfortable. When we choose to "pay God first," it's a tangible means by which we confirm our belief in His sovereign ownership. Further, such generosity tempers our joy in amassing resources or having nice things. It's not that having a home, car, or anything else is bad in and of itself; it becomes problematic, however, when we find our joy and self-identification in those things rather than in God.

Stewardship must be part of basic discipleship training and should be a routine, systematic, and continuing component of every church's discipleship strategy. Generous churches are built that way. Generous churches are the cumulative result of generous Christians who have learned how to manage God's money and resources wisely.

How much should people give in order to practice this necessary part of discipleship? The answer begins with the tithe. The tithe, 10 percent of gross income, is the foundation of personal giving for Christians today.

What three words come to mind when you hear the word "tithe"?

1.

2.

3.

What do those three words reveal about your feelings toward tithing?

Some argue tithing was an Old Testament concept, part of the law fulfilled by Jesus, therefore it is no longer applicable. That's a puzzling conclusion. When Jesus fulfilled the law, He filled it full in every way—He exceeded its requirements and demands. The same is true for tithing. Christian giving is grace giving—meaning more than the tithe and exceeding the requirements of the law. Christians have the privilege of giving according to their ability, exceeding the tithe, while preserving the principle of proportional giving from the resources God entrusts them.

When a person claims the tithe is no longer applicable, in a sense they are right. But only if they also believe the new standard exceeds the tithe, not as an excuse to give less.

If you were to begin looking at tithing as the minimum, how would your approach to generosity change?

Looking at the tithe as the base level of giving encourages people to take on opportunities to give even more and in various ways. The Antioch church gave a special offering to feed the hungry—meeting a basic human need. It's also likely they contributed financially to support the missionary teams they sent. Then they actually gave away their most valuable commodity—their leaders.

The spirit of such a transformational church is not, "How much can we keep?" but instead, "How much can we give away?" How the world would change if all churches developed that mind-set!

> **What specifically do you think would change about the reputation of the modern church if they adopted an attitude to Antioch's?**

There is no hard and fast rule about what an individual should give. The tithe establishes a guide or baseline for minimum giving. Beyond that, however, we must take on the attitude of the Antioch Christians who gave generously. They did not give because they had to but because they wanted to. In doing so, they experienced the joy and blessing of radical generosity. They became a world-changing church.

> **What are three ways this week you might begin to practice increased generosity?**
>
> 1.
>
> 2.
>
> 3.
>
> **How might you encourage your church to become more generous?**

1. Michael J. Wilkins, *The NIV Application Commentary: Matthew* (Grand Rapids, Michigan: Zondervan, 2004), 806.

SESSION 6

Be the Church!

SESSION 6

LAY THE FOUNDATION

1. Look back at the daily devotions you completed this week. Share one particular insight that was meaningful to you with your group.

2. How does understanding the difference between a steward and an owner promote generosity?

3. Which do you think was more difficult for the church at Antioch to give away—its money or its leaders? Why?

4. Do you think it's important to practice systematic discipline? What might be the spiritual advantage of doing so?

FRAME THE DISCUSSION

Watch the discussion starter on the DVD then discuss the following questions with your group.

1. If your church ceased to exist right now, what would be its lasting impact?

2. What about you? How do you hope to be eulogized?

3. How often do you think about your own personal legacy? Do you think it's healthy to think it through? Why or why not?

4. What will you remember most about the church at Antioch?

5. What practical things did the Antioch church do to ensure their legacy?

Watch the teaching segment from the DVD using the viewer guide below.

Eph 3:9
The church is God's ultimate purpose for the universe.

mystery:
a truth so profound it's incomprehensible apart from God

God has always been about the CREATION, preservation, and preparation of His church.

From Adam to Armageddon, God's UNIVERSAL work has all been about the church.

The church is the full revelation of God's WISDOM.

Eph 3:10
The church is a revelation of God's wisdom to the angels and demons in our world.

The church is the final and ultimate Outcome of the work of Jesus Christ.

The church is:

1. durable
2. holistic (Reaches out to everyone)
3. effective

Discuss the teaching segment with your group using the questions below.

1. Why do you think some people have such a low view of the church?

Reputation of Leaders
personally hurt
ARROGANCE
The church is a crutch

2. What would you say if someone asked you why, if they are a Christian, is it important they are involved in a local church?

3. In what ways have you seen your church be a revelation of God's wisdom?

4. What are some practical ways you might encourage other members of your church to have a higher view of the church?

Close with prayer.

FINISHING TOUCHES

Scripture Memory

> "You yourselves, as living stones, are being built into a spiritual house for a holy priesthood to offer spiritual sacrifices acceptable to God through Jesus Christ." **1 Peter 2:5**

Building Antioch

- Share with someone who was not a part of your study of Antioch a few things God has taught you over the past several weeks.
- Ask your pastor how you might specifically pray for your church moving forward.
- Pray about leading another small group through *Building Antioch*.

Video sessions are available for purchase at *www.lifeway.com/buildingantioch*

SESSION 6

Be the Church!

Perhaps examining the church at Antioch has been both an encouraging and a discouraging process for you. It's encouraging to see that transformed individuals can come together and create transformational churches that change the lives of their members, their communities, and the world.

But perhaps it has also been discouraging to you as you have recognized your church doesn't quite measure up to the standard set in Antioch. Though spiritual power, advancement of the gospel, commitment to the truth, and sacrificial generosity marked the believers of Antioch, your church may have a long way to go in those areas.

Be encouraged! The church—even though it is made up of imperfect people—is the final product, the complete outworking of God's redemptive plan through Christ. The immediate result of Jesus' life and work was the establishment of the first churches. Your church is part of that legacy, the continued result of God's ultimate plan.

Jesus' eternal legacy from His brief earthly sojourn is the church. His body, and someday, His bride. The New Testament makes it clear: The church is preeminent in God's eternal order. Furthermore, these scriptural realities don't describe some perfect church somewhere. They describe your church—with all its inadequacies and idiosyncrasies. Your church is the fulfillment of God's purpose for the universe. Your church is the full revelation of God's wisdom. Your church is the final outcome of Jesus' redemptive work. Thank God for your church!

Let's spend this final week examining some reasons why the church—your church—is unrivaled in its significance as part of the universe.

Day 1 The Body and the Bride

"Is it worth the effort?"

That's the question many people are asking about the church. For some, the answer is "no." The membership of most North American churches has either plateaued or is declining. That's not to say people are less interested in Christianity. Instead it points to a disassociation in the minds of modern believers between believing in Jesus and being an active part of a local church. Somehow, many Christians have developed the idea that church membership is an optional part of our faith. Because no church is perfect, more and more people do not see active membership as worth the effort.

Do you think it's important to be part of a local church? Why or why not?

How do you think God would respond to the question of whether church membership is worth the effort?

God did not intend active, joyful local church involvement to be an optional part of discipleship. This is rebutted by the use of two concepts in the Bible to describe the church. In Scripture, the church is referred to as both the body and the bride of Christ. Understanding these terms will broaden our understanding of the essential nature of the church.

Why do you think the church is referred to as "the body of Christ"?

What does that title indicate about the relationship between Jesus and the church?

Read 1 Corinthians 12:12-27. What are some of the implications you see in this passage about the church being the body of Christ?

Paul's point in the previous passage is the indispensability of every Christian in the church. The Corinthian believers had a tendency to attach greater importance to certain people and their spiritual gifts over others. Paul reminded them that in a body, the eye can't tell a finger or toe it's unimportant. Every part is important. Since we are the body of Christ, we must remember every Christian is uniquely gifted to serve a specific function in the church. Everyone matters!

It's important to note, however, Paul didn't tell the Corinthians they were *like* the body of Christ. Instead, he explicitly stated, "You are the body of Christ, and individual members of it" (1 Cor. 12:27). In a mysterious way, believers are unified by the indwelling Holy Spirit and become the functional body of Christ in our world. The church, as the body of Christ, is responsible for walking, talking, seeing, hearing, and acting as Jesus would act. We carry out His kingdom mission by working together, complementing one another, and fulfilling the ministry of Jesus.

What are three specific changes your church would make if its members really believed they are the body of Christ?

1.

2.

3.

In Revelation 21, John described the people of God meeting Jesus as a bride properly adorned and prepared to meet her husband. Jesus has betrothed Himself to His people, willingly sacrificing Himself for their well-being and eternal security, while awaiting the culmination of the relationship. He is absolutely faithful to His church in the meantime. He always acts for our good. He never stops loving us.

Christian marriage models the relationship between Christ and His church (see Eph. 5:22-33). Now imagine, for a moment, telling a devoted, loving husband you are quite fond of him but then leveling a barrage of insults at his wife. That is exactly what happens when you claim to love Jesus and yet not like—or even criticize—His church.

It's clear from these biblical images—the body and the bride—the church and Jesus can't be separated. Love them both, not one or the other. To be in Christ is to be in the church. To love Him is to love His bride. To do otherwise sullies them both.

With which idea do you connect more easily—the church as the body of Christ or the bride of Christ? Why?

Why is it important for Christians to see the church as both the body and the bride of Christ?

How would your church be different if every member looked at the church like this?

Day 2 A Durable Church

The fact that the church is still here testifies to God's faithfulness. The church is here to stay (until it migrates to heaven) and reigns eternally with God. The church on earth has lasted for about two thousand years. That's quite a track record for longevity.

What would you say are the three biggest challenges the church has endured in the last two thousand years?

1.

2.

3.

What challenges has your church endured? How have you overcome those challenges?

The church has endured doctrinal disasters, poor leadership, organizational mismanagement, and the waxing and waning of its missional commitment. The church has survived internal division and many external assaults. Spiritual warfare has consistently been waged against the church with devilish, relentless intensity. From time to time, this warfare has erupted into widespread persecution—even occasional attempts to extinguish the church altogether.

On the other extreme, the church has sometimes lost its spiritual way by exchanging missional purposes for the pseudosuperior trappings of governmental partnerships. The church has faced every kind of external opposition and internal distraction possible for two millennia. The church has endured through it all, just as Jesus said it would.

Read Matthew 16:13-16. If Jesus asked you the same question today, how would you answer?

How did Peter answer? Fill in the blanks below.

You are the ________________, the __________ of the living _________!

Read Matthew 16:17-19. According to Jesus, how was Peter able to make such a confession?

There was much confusion about the identity of Jesus during His time on earth. Was He a prophet? A teacher? A reincarnation of an Old Testament figure? Peter confessed the truth—Jesus is the Messiah, the Son of the living God. This confession is the same for all who enter into a relationship with God, whether first century fishermen or modern businesswomen. Christians first and foremost believe this—Jesus is Savior and Lord, the Messiah, Son of the living God.

How do you see Peter's confession linked to the church in this passage?

Though Peter was integral in the founding of the church, who really founded and now builds the church?

What did Jesus say about the durability of the church?

Peter, along with the other early apostles, played a key role in establishing the church. The church, Jesus promised, would endure through all time. No matter what happens, the church will still be around.

There's no other organization which enjoys such a promise. Governments will fall. Nations will topple. Humanitarian agencies and parachurch organizations will come and go. But the church will endure for all time.

Jesus, the Master Builder, has constructed His church so securely it can't be overcome by any assailant. When we align ourselves with the church, giving the church our allegiance, our support, and our love, we do so in confidence. We are assured the church will never, ever be destroyed.

What does the assurance of Jesus do for your commitment to the church? Why?

Knowing Jesus has thrown His full support behind the church, how should your attitude toward the church change?

What specific ways will you pray for your church this week in light of today's devotion?

BUILDING
ANTIOCH

Day 3 A Holistic Church

The church is not only unique in its durability, it's also one of the most holistic institutions, movements, societies, or associations ever created. Most organizations have certain qualifications required of their members. It might be a group only for athletes, women, students, retirees, gifted people, or those with significant resources. Not the church. The church, as an expression of God's wisdom, is a holistic movement welcoming everyone.

Read Ephesians 3:8-10. According to verse 10, what is revealed through the church?

Look up verse 10 in some other translations. What various words do you find in alternate translations for "multi-faceted"?

A diamond is multifaceted—carefully cut so that light refracts differently as it's slowly turned. It's a different stone from every angle. This example accentuates the tremendous variety in and among the people of God. The church emerges from and belongs in "every tribe and language and people and nation" (Rev. 5:9). It's a spiritual movement eclipsing racial, geographic, linguistic, and political distinctions. The church fits in every country, culture, and subculture.

Have you ever been to a church service in a culture different than your own? What was that experience like?

Why might being part of such an experience be important to your spiritual development?

The church is also multigenerational. All, from preschoolers to patriarchs, are welcome. The church is equally accessible for men and women—no gender restrictions are placed on redemption or membership. The church is also no respecter of persons related to talents, abilities, aptitudes, status, or wealth. In fact, the church is rare among modern organizations because it seeks out the broken, hurting, and victimized as objects of its mission.

The holistic nature of the church means everyone can be included. God's gift of salvation is available to all—not just the beautiful, wealthy, or influential. Church membership begins with redemption—a common experience for all believers—and isn't dependent on any accomplishment or status prior to regeneration. The church is for everyone.

Unfortunately, sometimes Christians have difficulty believing this important fact.

Think about your church. Would everyone in your city or town feel at home there? Why or why not?

Is it possible for a church to be accepting of people but not compromise its stance on moral issues? How?

Why is such a position important to take?

If we caught a glimpse of heaven, we would see the fullness of God's commitment to the holistic nature of the church. We would see heaven filled by an infinite variety of people from all demographics and cultures coming together to worship the Lamb of God. That's exactly what John saw in his vision of heaven.

Read Revelation 7:9-10. Describe the scene depicted in your own words.

Based on this description, would you be comfortable in that worship service? Why or why not?

John looked into eternity and saw multicolored faces staring back at him—the variety of the peoples of the earth, a holistic worshiping community set apart for the glory of Jesus. If we are Christians, then we're headed to that same kind of eternal worship service.

Why, then, are many churches today so monocultural? Why is there so little diversity in most congregations? Perhaps it's the natural result of people congregating with other like-minded believers, naturally working together to do their best but open to anyone who wants to join the effort. Unfortunately, sometimes it's because of intentional prejudice, excluding some believers because of language, race, or other differences. If your church is monocultural, be sure it fits the first category, never the second.

Since God is intentionally pursuing a holistic church, it seems reasonable we should make similar efforts. To do so, we must give up some of our personal preferences in regard to worship style and ministry programs, along with such practical matters like food served at church events. A diverse church is well worth the effort as we discover new dimensions of the body and bride of Jesus Christ.

Do you have close Christian friends from a culture different than your own?

What are some benefits of having friends like these?

What are some practical ways you might help your church be open to more diversity in its membership?

BUILDING
ANTIOCH

Day 4 An Effective Church

Jesus died to redeem mankind. This message—salvation is available for whoever comes to Jesus by grace through faith—has been entrusted to the church. Some might question God's wisdom in giving responsibility for sharing the gospel and extending the kingdom to such ordinary people. Nevertheless, history has proven the church is the best venue for disciple making and kingdom expansion.

This might not seem true, given the way many churches struggle to fulfill their mission. But take a global look. On some continents, the church is struggling. On others, it's thriving. God is moving through the global church, continually enlivening it and using it to fulfill His mission.

Why might being informed about the progress of the global church be important in the way you view your local church?

What makes the church so uniquely equipped to make disciples and expand the kingdom?

Churches are disciple-making organisms charged with forming the life of Jesus in believers. Local churches are spiritual formation laboratories. They shape character, confront sin, correct poor choices, and call people to a higher plan of living. While parachurch organizations specialize in assisting a segment of believers (like college students, military personnel, or athletes) churches disciple everyone. God has specifically and uniquely equipped churches for this task.

Read Ephesians 4:10-16. Describe how the church is meant to function toward the end goal of discipleship.

According to verse 11, how has Jesus proven His support for the church's efforts in discipleship?

To what end are the church leaders meant to exercise their gifts?

Jesus has personally equipped people to lead the ministry of the church. Their job is not merely to teach, preach, administrate, or motivate—they are tasked with the eternally important outcome of producing disciples. Those believers, having been trained by their leaders, actually participate in the work of ministry, building up the body of Christ until all believers reach a state of maturity. Because this work is done in and through the body of Christ, there is no viable replacement for local churches as the centerpiece of God's strategic disciple-making methodology.

According to verse 14, what is the effect of growing into Christian maturity?

Why is that kind of growth needed, especially in the current culture?

With the competing belief systems in the world today, where everyone seems to be spiritual in one way or another, the church is charged as the guardian of the true gospel. It's through the disciple-making work of the church that men and women, regardless of where they might have come from, grow into the image of Christ.

The end result of discipleship is that people are able to stand against the ever-blowing winds of cultural change as well as continually bless others through the maturing work of the church. For two millennia, the church has been the mechanism through which spiritual maturity happens most regularly and effectively. That plan is not about to change now.

If you are a church-detractor, a simple question is, "What is your alternative strategy?" It must be a comprehensive strategy—for everyone, not just a select group. It must also be an eternal strategy—timeless and timely in every era. It's easy to take shots at the church. It's much harder to create a workable alternative. Rather than waste unproductive time demeaning the church, your efforts are more wisely expended reforming, refining, and realigning your church with God's mission.

Doing so takes more patience and commitment than being a critic. Local churches, even when they struggle, are still God's best laboratory for turning people into fully devoted followers of Jesus and preparing them to be God's eternal companions.

Have you recently been critical of your church? Why?

How might your efforts be redirected toward forming your church into a more biblical expression of the body of Christ?

Day 5 The Church Needs You

Transformational churches like Antioch don't just happen. They emerge because individual members are being transformed daily by the work of God in their lives. As part of His work, those believers have recognized God delights in the church and local churches. They are convinced God has called them to church membership. They fully give themselves to their church, making every effort to do their part in helping their community of faith be all it can be.

Read Romans 12:1-8. How do verses 1-2 relate to verses 3-8?

Does your view of verses 1-2 change when you read them in the context of the rest of the passage?

What, according to this passage, is God's "good, pleasing, and perfect will" for you?

Often, we focus on the first two verses of this passage. We see the need to daily offer our bodies "as a living sacrifice, holy and pleasing to God." Furthermore, we believe doing so is our "spiritual worship." Likewise, we believe we must walk in a countercultural fashion, refusing to "be conformed to this age" but instead choosing to have our minds renewed and therefore transformed.

But if we keep reading we will see this command is understood in the context of the church rather than as individuals. Offering ourselves as a sacrifice leading to transformation is something meant to be experienced corporately—not in isolation. Paul wrote active participation in the church is the context where we find God's good, pleasing, and perfect will for our lives.

God's will includes finding our place in the church, devoting ourselves fully to it, and playing our part in the church's mission in the world.

What are some obstacles for people fulfilling their part in the mission of the church?

How might those obstacles be overcome?

Paul's exhortation is based on the fact that no individual person can play every role in the church, just as one part of the body cannot perform all the functions necessary for life. Indeed, the body only functions properly when each of its parts functions at peak operating condition. Similarly, the church can't reach its potential until every Christian is willing to embrace his or her God-given responsibility in the larger Christian community.

We all have a part to play, and it's a role for which we have been uniquely gifted. Not everyone is a teacher. Nor is everyone gifted with mercy, encouragement, or service. According to Paul, that's exactly how it's supposed to be. The church is where all those various gifts come together to form a complete unit, one body fully equipped to disciple believers and expand the kingdom of God throughout the entire world.

What are your spiritual gifts?

If you don't know, why is it important you find out?

What are some steps you might take to see your gifts more fully used in your church?

It's only when we know our gifts, embrace them, and use them for the greater good that the church can be all it is intended to be. Unfortunately, too many of us are sitting idly in our gifts, using them for our personal gain, or even ignoring how the Spirit has gifted us. If that's the case, we are depriving ourselves the joy of serving in the body of Christ—and also depriving our church an essential member it needs for effective ministry.

That's not God's will for your life. His will is for you to see the church as a people worthy of your affection and devotion and to impact the world by serving in and through your church.

God loves the church. He loves your church. He has called you, no matter who you are, to give yourself to the church—His most prized possession, His eternal companion, and the object of His ultimate purpose. You are part of shaping the destiny of the universe. What could be more worthwhile as a life investment? Thank God for the church ... and for your church! Give your best effort to help create a person-changing, community-changing, world-changing church. Give your best and your all to create a transformational church!